THOMAS TELFORD

Thomas Telford

————⋙⬤⬤⬤⬤⬤⬤⬤⬤⬤⬤⬤⬤⬤⬤⋘————

ANTHONY BURTON

AURUM PRESS

First published in 1999
by Aurum Press Ltd
25 Bedford Avenue, London WC1B 3AT

A catalogue record for this book is available from the British Library.

ISBN 1 85410 652 X

1 3 5 7 9 10 8 6 4 2
1999 2001 2003 2002 2000

Design by Roger Lightfoot
Typeset by Action Publishing Technology
Printed and bound in Great Britain by
Creative Print and Design Group, Wales

Contents

Acknowledgements

In Chapter Four, the signed sketch of the unlikely design for an aqueduct is reproduced courtesy of the Science and Society Picture Library. All other drawings included within the text are reproduced courtesy of the Institution of Civil Engineers.

The maps in the gazetteer section are by Don Macpherson.

Preface

My interest in Thomas Telford was first aroused around forty years ago
when my wife and I set off, somewhat nervously, to steer across the mighty
aqueduct of Pontcysyllte. At that time it was universally attributed to
Telford, an attribution I was happy to repeat in my book *The Canal
Builders*. Some years later I was approached by a publisher who asked if I
would consider writing a new biography of Telford. I refused, on the not
unreasonable grounds that everything that needed to be said about the
man had already been said, and probably better than I could say it, by
L. T. C. Rolt. I had, and have, the greatest admiration for Rolt, enhanced
by the encouragement he gave to my work on *The Canal Builders*. The
thought of competing was beyond contemplation.

It was another of the pioneers of transport history, Charles Hadfield,
who began to put doubts in my mind. The publication in 1979 of the biography of William Jessop that he wrote with A. W. Skempton put a very
strong case for rethinking the story of Pontcysyllte. Over the years Charles
kept ringing up, rather gleefully, to say that he had found out something
else about 'my man' – quite how Telford had become 'my man' I was not
sure. That process culminated in Charles's last book, *Thomas Telford's
Temptation*. It was now clear that re-evaluation was becoming necessary,
and that perhaps the time had come to take up the challenge I had earlier
rejected.

There has been an unhappy tendency among a minority of biographers
in recent years to claim that their work is somehow better than that of their
predecessors because they have been able to correct 'mistakes'. What this
usually amounts to is the discovery of previously unknown material that
demands a rethinking of the story of the past. This happens all the time; if
it did not, there would be little need for the new work at all. When I started work on this book, I was very conscious of just how much I owed to my
predecessor. The very first thing I did was to reread Rolt, and enjoyed it as

much as I had ever done. I was nervous, but not unhappy about starting. For one thing I felt very strongly was that if he were alive today, he too would be rethinking parts of the story – and would have been getting the calls from Charles instead of me! The work of L. T. C. Rolt has been an inspiration to me throughout my professional career as an author, and I hope those who read this book will see it not as a replacement of his work but as a necessary continuation. My one sadness is that Charles is not here to argue about some of my opinions – and argue he surely would have done. All I can do is to dedicate this book to the memory of two great pioneers of transport and engineering history, L. T. C. Rolt and Charles Hadfield.

Anthony Burton
Stroud, 1998

Introduction

Biographies are often entitled 'The Life and Work' of whoever the subject might be. In Telford's case it might be more appropriate to refer to 'The Work and Life of Thomas Telford', for that is surely the order in which he himself would have placed them. He worked continuously from the day he began as a boy, almost until the day he died, and it is by his works that he would want to be remembered. There is enough testimony by those who knew him to suggest that his was an affable character when he relaxed in company, but the truth is that relaxation was a luxury for which he had all too little time. One of the frustrations of writing this book at first was the lack of information about his private life. Grateful as one is to the likes of Robert Southey for his detailed account of accompanying Telford on the inspection of his engineering works, and for passing on what they looked like and what the engineer had to say about them, one cannot help wishing most fervently that he had told us what else they talked about. Similarly, Telford himself had very little time for letter writing, apart from official correspondence, but his private letters, mostly to the Little family, do at least give us a strong feel for his personality. Yet, while researching this book and hunting for information, it became steadily clearer how futile it was to try and separate the man from his work; engineering quite simply was his life, and there was little room left for anything else.

At first, I felt concerned that the engineering works were overwhelming the man, but as I went on, that worry began to disappear. More and more I realised just what a heroic life it was, how taxing both physically and intellectually. I became ever more impressed by the sheer range of challenges that Telford accepted and met. It is, I am aware, deeply unfashionable to consider the subject of engineering as anything other than terminally dull. In that case, I can only plead guilty to being hopelessly out of fashion. I have found in Telford a man who could not only solve problems, but could do so in wholly original ways. No plodding mentality could have done so; even to conceive of such structures as the Menai bridge required a huge act of imagination. To bring them to reality required a great deal more. So, to the reader looking for salacious gossip, I am sorry – there is none. To those who hope to find Freudian analysis of a celibate who lost himself in work, I am afraid there is no such analysis. All that I have tried to do is to give a picture of what it meant to be one of the world's greatest engineers at a time of the most profound changes. That seemed challenge enough for any biographer.

CHAPTER ONE

The Shepherd's Son

—————⋙∎∎∎∎∎∎∎∎∎∎⋘—————

Thomas Telford was born in a cottage by the Meggat Water which gurgles down between grassy banks to Eskdale and the River Esk in the Scottish southern uplands. If you want to visit his birthplace, you take the minor road that winds up the valley of the Esk from Langholm, mimicking each turn of the river as it goes, until it reaches the little hamlet of Bentpath. There, at the roadside, are a pair of angular, not very comfortable stone benches with a somewhat severe Thomas Telford looking out from a plaque in between. Not an inappropriate memorial, perhaps, for a man who began his working life here as a stonemason, and there is a verse of Telford's to provide further justification:

> There 'mongst these rocks I'll form a rural seat
> And plant some ivy with its moss compleat
> I'll benches form of fragments from the stone
> Which nicely pois'd was by your hand o'erthrown.

But you have not yet reached the actual birthplace. You must turn off this lonely road for one even lonelier, following Meggat Water, seemingly on its way to nowhere other than a vast swelling of hills, undulating away to the horizon. Just before it peters out at the tiny settlement of Glendinning at the foot of Kirk Cleuch Rig, the road passes a small oblong patch of conifers. In the darkness of the close-packed trees, now almost totally lost from sight, is a jumble of stones, all that remains of the cottage that was home to the shepherd John Telford and his wife Janet.

This is a Scotland that few know, a region that the busy traffic bustles through on its way to Glasgow and Edinburgh. Tourists find little to detain them here, and even walkers tend to head for the more dramatic rocky peaks and crags of the Highlands. Those who do come this way, perhaps walking the long-distance Southern Upland Way path that passes a few miles to the north, find an amazingly empty, thinly populated landscape, where it is still possible to walk all day without meeting another human being. There have been changes, notably in the great blankets of forest thrown over the land, but elsewhere one finds a landscape scarcely changed in the two-and-a-half centuries since Telford was born here on 9 August 1757. If the area does not possess the stark grandeur of the Highlands, it has its own beauty in the steady recession of billowing hills. The area does not look like the Highlands, and it was not merely geography that was different two-and-a-half centuries ago.

Scotland at the start of the eighteenth century was a land of two parts. To the north were the Highlands, Gaelic-speaking, organised as they had been for centuries into clans who, when not actually fighting each other, lived in a state of mutual distrust. The richer lands to the south supported a more settled and certainly more prosperous community – though there remained the history of border raiders or reivers, among whom was a certain Jamie Telford. The Act of Union of 1707 which joined together England and Scotland brought calmer times and was generally accepted in the south. The north remained largely isolated and was only drawn on to the national scene when the clans disastrously rallied to the banner of Bonnie Prince Charlie. After that cause was finally lost on the bloody moor of Culloden, the English and their Scottish allies exacted their retribution and set in train a programme of vicious suppressions. The Highlanders were to pay for their part in the Jacobite rebellions with years of misery and impoverishment. This was the land into which Telford was born, just eleven years after Culloden.

The birth of Thomas must have been a particularly happy event for the Telfords, for there had been an earlier Thomas born who had not survived. There is no record of this child, other than the carving on a tombstone. The parents' happiness was short-lived, for John Telford himself died on 12 November 1757 and it is on his gravestone that the name of the other Thomas is recorded. The death of the father was a double blow. Not only had the wage-earner been taken from the young family, but they now had to leave the house to make way for the new shepherd. In the summer of 1758, Janet and her young son moved a mile and a half down the valley to the cottage of Crooks. They no longer had a whole house to themselves, but just one room, and here Janet was to stay until her death in 1794. Inevitably, the family had to look for charity, and they were helped by her brother, Mr Jackson. This could not have come easily to Janet, seemingly a woman of stern principles, of whom her son was always rather in awe. In his later, more prosperous years, he regularly sent her money, but had to do so through a third party, an old friend, Andrew Little. Even then, it seemed she would rather struggle on with the little she had rather than accept gifts from her own son, a fact which grieved him greatly: 'her habits of economy will prevent her getting plenty of everything especially as she thinks I have to pay for it which really hurts me more than anything else'.[1] If she was unwilling to accept help from him, then one can reasonably assume that only real necessity allowed her to accept charity from her other relations. But she had no choice and some of the money went to providing her young son with a basic education at the village school. It was here that he met and became friends with the two brothers, William and Andrew Little.

Not very much is known about his boyhood. Like most children in his circumstances, hours not spent in the classroom were employed helping out local farmers. In the summer months in particular, this would have involved long hours out on the hills and unremitting hard work: good training for a future life which was to be filled with both commodities. From casual references in his letters and notes to his autobiography, it is clear that whatever he felt at the time, he looked back on those days as a happy period in his life. After he had left the region, he kept in regular touch with the Littles and was always pleased to hear of the friends of his boyhood days, joking about 'the glutton boy' John Elliot and Jennie Smith – 'tell her she is a canterrin sort of lassie'.[2] He also celebrated his native Eskdale in verse which presents a picture of a rather conventional rural idyll, expressed in equally conventional terms.[3]

> Deep 'mid the green sequester'd glens below
> Where murmuring streams among the alders flow
> Where flowery meadows down their margins spread
> And the brown hamlet lifts its humble head
> There, round his little fields, the peasant strays
> And sees his flock along the mountain graze.

Memory, as selective as ever, seems to have mislaid the days of wild winds and unrelenting rain which anyone who has spent much time in these hills would recall all too vividly. The important point is that he wanted to celebrate the good days and the happy days, perhaps precisely because they could not last. It was a great good fortune for the children of the poor if they received any education at all – but once the rudiments had been hammered in, then it was time to start the serious business of earning a living. For many it was a transition to a life of drudgery as a farm hand or labourer, or perhaps a journey to one of the new textile mills being developed in the surrounding region. But for young Telford it was the start of a quite different journey, that was to set him on his way to learning a valuable trade. He became apprenticed to a stonemason in Lochmaben.

What a contrast Lochmaben must have seemed to the peaceful glen, even if it was only a day's walk away. It seems a modest enough place today, but it was once a royal burgh, with a charter dating back to the thirteenth century. The medieval castle rose up on a rocky promontory above the broad main street, and there were tales enough to please a small boy. Robert the Bruce had lived there, and, even more excitingly, the old sixteenth-century tower house was said to have a chain-clanking ghost in the dungeon. Telford's stay, however, was short; the boy was so badly mistreated that he returned home. It was not an auspicious start, but once again the Jackson family came to the rescue, this time in the form of Thomas Jackson, steward to the Johnstones of Westerhall, a man well placed to find a suitable niche, and one a good deal nearer to home. Now young Thomas was apprenticed to a Langholm mason, Andrew Thomson. He was doubly fortunate: he not only found a kind and skilled master, but he found himself in a bustling trade where important works were taking place.

The land around Langholm was mostly owned by the Duke of Buccleuch. Like so many Scottish landowners at that time, he was a great 'improver': unlike too many others, however, he believed in improving the lot of the people of the region and not simply increasing his own profits. In place of the old cottages of mud walls and heather thatch, he built houses of stone with slate roofs, boasting the previously unimaginable luxury of what Telford rather coyly referred to as 'convenient offices'. The area is still shown on modern maps as 'New Langholm'. There were other changes introduced, which meant more work for the local masons:[4]

Regular Roads were constructed for the old horse tracks and wheel carriages introduced. Bridges were made over the mountain streams, those, altho' numerous, were generally small. They, however, furnished employment to the practical Artizans, and I was here early experienced in the several operations required in their construction.

It was not only that there was a good deal of work in hand, but it was just the sort of work that was to stand him in good stead for the future.[5]

> In that Country therefore, convenience and utility only are studied – Yet by these some peculiar advantages are afforded to the young practitioner – there not being sufficient employment to induce a division of labour in the several building branches, he is under the necessity of making himself acquainted with many operations in procuring, preparing and using many sorts of material from the forest, the quarry and the forge.

The most important work in which Telford was involved was the new bridge across the Esk at Langholm. By the time it was built, around 1778, Telford's apprenticeship had ended; he was now a fully fledged journeyman with his own mason's mark. The bridge still stands, a handsome structure carried on three rather flat segmental arches, with piers of roughly dressed stone. It was widened in 1880 but remains substantially as it was, and the young Telford's mason's marks can be seen close to the water line under the western arch.

Samuel Smiles, the popular biographer of the great engineers[6] and an enthusiastic collector of colourful anecdotes, had a number of stories about this stage of Telford's life – some of which are, to say the least, more than a little dubious. They probably grew extra details over the years. One story told of Andrew Thomson's wife Tibby, frantic with worry as flood waters swept down the Esk through Langholm with a roar and swirl of brown, peaty water. Her husband was away from home and, fearful that his newly completed masterpiece was about to be carried away by the floods, she dashed down to the river crying for help from Tammy Telford. The young mason trotted up to find her putting her back to the abutments as if by her own force alone she could keep the bridge standing. The young man, according to Smiles, found the whole episode hilariously funny. Smiles thought so too, but a modern reader cannot help thinking that laughing at the distracted woman was less than charitable and, as the lady happened to be his employer's wife, less than sensible. There is also evidence to suggest that Thomson was not even involved with the bridge, and that it was actually the work of another local mason, Robin Hotson, for whom Telford was working at the time. It does, however, point up a side of Telford's character that all who knew him seemed to note: his cheerful disposition and sense of humour. Another anecdote points to another aspect of his character:

the great pride he took in the practical skills of the craftsman, skills which he had mastered after a long training. In 1795, he returned to Eskdale, already well established in a new career as an engineer and architect – but not so well established that he could be sure of keeping his new high status. Here he met an old friend and fellow workman Frank Beattie, who had abandoned masonry for the rather less arduous work of an innkeeper.[7]

> 'What have you made of your mell and chisels?' asked Telford.
> 'Oh!' replied Beattie, 'they are all dispersed – perhaps lost.'
> 'I have taken better care of mine,' said Telford. 'I have them all locked up in a room at Shrewsbury, as well as my old working clothes and leather apron: you know one can never tell what may happen.'

True or not, at least part of the story is in character. Even in his days of greatness, Telford never lost sight of the fact that what he knew, he knew from experience. He understood materials because he had worked them with his own hands, and worked them well. At this distance in time, it would have been difficult to assess the quality of his workmanship were there not examples still to be seen today. His father was buried in the churchyard at Westerkirk, now Bentpath, with a plain stone to mark the grave. Telford had taught himself letter carving, and as soon as he felt confident in his abilities he set to work to carve an inscription. This is a very different craft from squaring up blocks of stone for a bridge. The inscription itself is simple: 'In Memory of John Telford who after thirty three Years as an unblameable shepherd died in Glendinning 13 Nov 1757: his son Thomas who died an infant'. The lettering is neat, with no great flourishes, but expertly executed with smooth curves emphasised by the varying thickness of the strokes and well-defined serifs. A few paces away is a second memorial by Telford. This commemorates the Pasley family, starting with James Pasley and ending with Elizabeth Pasley, who died in 1790, a lady to whom Telford owed a great deal. The family were wealthy and Elizabeth Pasley's passion was literature, an enthusiasm she was keen to share with others. The young mason had an enquiring mind and ambitions of doing more with his life than remaining a journeyman in a quiet village. The Scots have always had a reputation for placing a greater emphasis on education than their southern neighbours, and Telford must have known that a good education eased the way forward in life. It was not merely a case of learning 'useful' skills, but also of being at one's ease with other educated people. There is no record of why he decided to take advantage of the offer to read as widely as he wished in the extensive Pasley library, but we do know the results.

The first book he read, or at least the first book that profoundly interested him, was Milton's *Paradise Lost*. This is an immense work in every sense: it contains over 10,000 lines of verse and deals with the greatest of themes, the battle between good and evil. It is a work that few people today open, let alone read from end to end, so what must it have meant to a young man, whose working life was concerned with the physical rather than the metaphysical? The first thing that strikes any reader is the extraordinary rhythmic power of the language: once you are captured by those rolling cadences, they carry you onward with an unremitting momentum. Some find themselves unmoved and give up, but for those with a natural disposition to enjoy words for their own sake and who respond to imagery and rhythm, it is all but irresistible. Telford found himself to be one of those who are enraptured by Milton. He could not say what it was, only 'I read and read, and glowered, then read and read again'. 'Glowered' is a good word, because there is that quality in Milton, rather as one might find in Beethoven: they are not there to be taken lightly.

The discovery of a delight in poetry is not essential for the life of an engineer, but it did help to awaken the young man to a wider world of ideas. His early enthusiasm for Milton gave way to a more conventional taste for his contemporaries, particularly those who had something serious to say, or an improving moral to impart – writers such as William Cowper and Robert Southey. He also began to write verse, not usually very well, and he seems to have known that himself. He was supremely confident when it came to his practical life, but only nervously sent off his efforts to friends and was quick to accept criticism. He wrote rather self-deprecatingly of his poetry that 'it is to me, something like what a fiddle is to others, I apply to it in order to relieve the mind after being much fatigued with close attention to business'.[8] Nevertheless, he thought highly enough of his efforts to send them off for publication – and had the gratification of seeing some, at least, accepted. Poetry was important in his life, and if it did nothing else it set him apart from his fellow workmen – he was a man to notice.

Telford had good friends in Eskdale who were to remain staunch allies, and some, notably his fellow mason, Matthew Davidson, were to go on to become trusted colleagues, but he was aware that his future could not be limited to the opportunities available at home. In 1780, he set off on foot to find work at Edinburgh, and again he was fortunate in his timing. Medieval Edinburgh had grown up on the high rocky ridge dominated by the castle. The town grew and grew until, by the mid-eighteenth century, there was no space for it to grow any more. Beneath the castle rock was the 'Nor' Lock', a wide sheet of water that ended in a swampy morass. The town council, under Lord Provost Drummond, paid for the whole area to be drained – creating what is now Princes Street Gardens – and threw a bridge across to join the castle rock to good dry land on the far side. Here a young architect, James Craig, laid out the New Town. It was a strictly formal arrangement with two squares linked by a central road, George Street, flanked by Queen Street and Princes Street and joined by cross streets to make a uniform grid. Everything was new, and everywhere the architecture showed the Georgian style at its finest. Telford left no record of his reactions when faced with this display of elegance, but the effect must have been as overwhelming as discovering Milton. Recollecting it more soberly in later life when writing his autobiography, he merely noted two new discoveries. He was introduced to 'the Art of delineating Architecture upon Paper', which was quite different from anything he had known in Eskdale, where building followed established practice, handed down by experience from journeyman to apprentice. He seems to have grasped the importance of this art almost immediately, setting himself to study the mysteries of plans and elevations. And he also found a new type of building that could be 'appropriated to the progress of magnificence as well as utility'. No doubt he added to his practical masonry skills during this stay in Edinburgh, but, more importantly, he experienced a fresh widening of his intellectual horizons.

He returned to Eskdale at the end of 1781, but it was only a brief stay. He now knew that his future lay in a wider world. He said goodbye to his mother and friends and in January 1782 set off for London. He was twenty-four years old and full of self-confidence, as he had every reason to be. He had proved himself a master of his chosen craft, and had entered the wider world of art and ideas, a world in which he was beginning to feel equally at home. He was no longer the country boy gawping at the wonders of the great city: he had seen a new world being created in his nation's capital and had had a part in its making. He had learned to think for himself in matters of taste and judgement, as well as in those practical questions of how to dress a stone or create an arch. Eskdale was left behind, but not forgotten.

Poetry provided another outlet for him, not just in the manner of an evening playing the fiddle by the fire, but as a way of expressing emotions that might have seemed maudlin in prose.[9]

> Yet still one voice, while fond remembrance stays,
> One feeble voice, shall celebrate thy praise;
> Shall tell thy sons that, wheresoe'r they roam,
> The hermit Peace hath built her cell at home;
> Tell them, Ambition's wreath, and Fortune's gain,
> But ill supply the pleasures of the plain;
> Teach their young hearts thy simple charms to prize,
> To love their native hills, and bless their native skies.

CHAPTER TWO

To England

————⫸⫷⫸————

The interest that the young man had shown in Elizabeth Pasley's books was now more than repaid by the interest she took in her protégé. He arrived in London with an introduction to her brother, a successful merchant, John Pasley, who in turn was able to pass on introductions to the two most famous architects of the day, Sir William Chambers and Robert Adam. Recalling them in later life, Telford gave thumbnail sketches of the two men:[1]

> The former was distant and haughty the latter affable and kind, and a similar characteristic seems to pervade their works, Sir William being stiff and formal, those of Mr Adam playful and gay – and altho' from neither did I derive any distinct advantage, yet so powerful in manner, that the latter left the most favourable impression.

Very few would argue with his critical judgement of the two men and their work. Both had studied in Rome and were associated with the classical revival, but Adam brought a lightness and dash to his work, a love of delicate, intricate decoration that makes his best buildings almost rococo. Chambers's work, as Telford knew it, followed rather strictly along the formal lines laid down by Palladio. Yet it was Chambers who provided London with one of its most famously flamboyant and exotic buildings, the pagoda at Kew Gardens, for he had visited China before he went to Rome. By the time Telford made his acquaintance, however, he was official architect to the royal family, a purveyor of solemn premises for serious purposes.

It was not quite true that Telford derived no advantage from the introduction to Chambers: it gave him the opportunity to work on the most prestigious new building in London. Construction of Somerset House had begun in 1775. It was intended from the first to hold government offices, and Chambers designed a suitably stiff and formal building for the bureaucrats. If the whole effect is of monumentality unrelieved by any overall sense of elegance, there are plenty of good details and satisfying flourishes. There was, in short, plenty of artistic work for a skilful craftsman. Telford went to work, supremely confident that his powers were equal to the task.

Fortunately, we know a good deal about Telford's life at this time. Among the friends who had left Eskdale to find a better life was Andrew Little. He had preceded Telford in moving to Edinburgh, where he had studied medicine, and on qualifying had found a berth as a ship's doctor on an African slaver. The voyage was a personal disaster. A bolt of lightning hit the ship in a storm and left Little permanently blinded. His life in medicine was over, and he returned to Langholm to take up the job of village schoolmaster. Telford, as soon as he reached London, began a regular correspondence, far more prolific than he maintained at any other time in his life. If it was an act of charity to brighten the life of his stricken friend, it was charity that was never allowed to show. The letters are bright and cheerful, full of incident and news, and never once refer to the fact that their recipient was blind. They are all written directly and personally, with no hint that they would have to be read to him by a third party. Throughout his life, Telford was ready to help out friends in many different ways, but his good nature never appears in a better light than in the Little letters.

Telford was set to work on the south-west corner of Somerset House, an area where Chambers seemed to have used every device in the architectural book. A pilastered façade runs above a rusticated base, pedimented windows stand above arches and the whole is topped by a heavily dentilled cornice and balustrade ornamented with urns – no shortage of work for stone carvers. He was certainly not intimidated by what he saw – far from it. He was soon writing home to tell his friends they should expect to hear great things of him.[2]

> I am laying schemes of a pretty extensive kind if they succeed, for you know my disposition is not to be satisfied unless when plac'd in some conspicuous Point of view my innate vanity is too apt to say when looking on the Common drudges here as well as other places Born to command ten thousand Slaves like you.

He elaborated, pointing out that the local workmen were more ignorant than those of Eskdale – 'not a M. David^n – among them', though he grudgingly added 'not best but they do seem to do their work surprisingly well'. He was undeniably vain, but was at least open about it – and it was vanity based on justifiable self-confidence.

The grand scheme he had in mind involved one of the other workmen, Hatton, who had been working at Somerset House from the start. While Hatton had become the acknowledged expert on the most intricate carvings in stone and marble, his rate of pay was scarcely more than that of the ordinary journeymen around him.

> The Master he works under looks on him as the principal support of his business but I'll tear away that Pillar if my scheme succeeds, and let the Old beef head and his puppy of an ignorant Clerk try their dexterity at their leisure.

Telford had 'kindled a spark in his breast', encouraging him to believe that if the two of them went into partnership, they could take contracts on their own behalf. Robert Adam encouraged them in the enterprise, but Telford still had to make sure that he also had the approval of Chambers. There was, in any case, a major snag. It was all very well taking out lucrative contracts, but they would expect to wait up to two years before the money came in – and, in the meantime, how were they to live? An inconvenient little problem that he was quite unable to solve, and the partnership was never formed. The spark may have been struck, but the flame was destined never to be kindled. It was perhaps as well, for Telford was about to make a new connection that was to prove to mark one of the great turning points in his life. And once again the habit of Eskdale to look after its own was to prove its worth.

Westerhall was a grand house very close to Telford's old home, and its owner Sir James Johnstone decided it was in need of improvement. Perhaps it was the Jackson family who suggested Telford as a likely candidate, but in any case Sir James wrote to his younger brother William in London, suggesting they discuss the work. If Sir James was grand, his brother was now even grander, having married into the Pulteney family of Bath, very sensibly changing his own name to Pulteney on doing so. The family name is still remembered in the Bath region, notably for the famous Pulteney Bridge that crosses the Avon in the centre of the city, but this represented only a part of their immense wealth. Apart from their estate in Somerset, they also had considerable interests in Northamptonshire and Shropshire. In the normal way of life in the eighteenth century, one would not expect one of the richest men in Britain to have a great deal to say to a prospective employee, who after all was at this stage of his career no more than a journeyman mason. It must have come as something of a surprise to Pulteney to find a well-educated, articulate man who not only understood architectural drawings but also had his own opinions on architectural taste. Telford, for his part, found a man ready to judge others on their merits, not their social position, a man wholly devoid of ostentation. He was later to sum up his views of Pulteney:[3]

> His manner is remarkably engaging – and how comes it to be so? Why by that plain simplicity and natural ease which ought to be the study of all men, the moment that is departed from, there is something which takes place which is disgusting. Mr Pulteney is a man who does not court popularity, he is distant and cautious and reserved to mankind in general, but I believe to the few in whom he can confide there is no man more open.

Fortunately, it was a quiet time for Telford. One government had gone and another, under the younger Pitt, had taken over, and the resulting policy changes had meant a reduction in funds for public building. So, there was nothing to stop him working on the Westerhall scheme. As a result, he and Pulteney met two or three times a day to discuss the changes, while Telford fired off endless queries to Little about the cost of labour and materials in Eskdale as he prepared the detailed estimates. All went smoothly, sufficiently so for Telford to be offered a second commission. This was an age when wealthy landowners such as Pulteney had a great many benefits to bestow, including livings to clergymen. It is easy to forget when looking at the life of a busy engineer that this was also the age of Jane Austen, and the disposal of livings is crucial to the story in more than one of her novels. In this case, the living was that of Sudborough in Northamptonshire and the vicar was the Rev. Archibald Alison. He was about to be married, and Pulteney felt that improvements were needed before the bride could move into the vicarage. Telford took on the work and in the process acquired a new friend and, usefully for biographers, a new correspondent. In Alison he also found a sounding board against which to try out his ideas on literature and a critic who could be relied upon to give an honest – sometimes it must have seemed too honest – view of his own verse. In 1799, Telford penned a truly atrocious poem on Shakespeare's Avon. A short sample should satisfy anyone:[4]

Thy Shakespeare was the first of Bards
His like the nations never saw.
He draws to thee our true regards,
Thy sacred banks we tread with care.

Alison told the aspiring poet what he thought of it, and the verses were consigned to the wastepaper basket.

These small building jobs not only filled in the time before the next project, but also gave Telford the chance of working as his own master, answerable only to his client; all valuable experience. He did not, however, have to wait long before the next major job appeared. Whilst working at Somerset House, Telford would have come into contact with one of the important contractors, Samuel Wyatt, a lesser-known member of a prodigious family of architects, who was now involved with the large-scale improvements of the naval dockyard at Portsmouth. During the eighteenth century, great areas of the foreshore were reclaimed and made useable, increasing the area of the dockyard from 10.5 to 33 hectares, and there was an accompanying rush of building, including docks, stores and roperies. It was one of the busiest places in the land and in some ways the most adventurous, making it a good proving ground for engineers. So, it is not perhaps surprising that one finds the connection occurring over and over again. So that, for example, by the end of the century Marc Brunel was based here establishing his revolutionary block-making equipment, and his more famous son, Isambard, was born here, destined later to compete successfully against the then elderly Telford for one of the great engineering prizes of the day. And it does not end there, for Isambard was to co-operate with one of the next generation of Wyatts, Matthew Digby Wyatt, in the design of Paddington Station. This is not meant as an example of amazing coincidences, but rather as an indication that when Telford came to work at Portsmouth's naval dockyard he was entering a world where important work was in hand, attracting important engineers and architects, and where he could add still more to his growing store of knowledge and experience.

It is not clear whether he came to the docks through the Wyatt connection or not, but the scale of new work must have become generally known to the artisans kicking their heels at Somerset House, waiting for work to pick up. Equally, it could have done no harm to Telford's chances that he came with a recommendation from one of the richest and most influential men in the land. Patronage meant as much in the port as in the parsonage. In any case, whether the job was his entirely on personal merit or with a little friendly assistance, he was soon unpacking his bags in Portsmouth.

When Telford started work, he began at a higher rung up the ladder than that which he had occupied in London, and soon was to climb higher still. As with many major projects, there was a complex structure of command. On the one hand were the Navy and the Portsmouth officers, who naturally took a considerable interest in their developing base. The actual construction was carried out by a civilian work force under the control of Wyatt, but ultimate responsibility for seeing it was properly carried out lay with the admiralty surveyor, J. Marquand. But this was by no means the only work for which Marquand was responsible, and there were complaints from the local controller, Henry Martin, that there was insufficient supervision of the project on a day-to-day basis. Telford was already in charge of part of the works, including a chapel and the Commissioner's House, a building of considerable grandeur which, among its other functions, was intended to house royalty and foreign dignitaries. He was a likely candidate for the post, but a certain amount of discreet tactical manoeuvring was necessary. He wrote frankly about his ambitions, and of the difficult and dangerous balancing act he would have to perform in appearing to serve several masters with equal diligence.[5]

We are going on briskly here with our Buildings. I have got the new Chapel fairly above ground and shall cover it in this Season: this fine Commissioner's House we are going on with the inside finishing &c. so that amongst all I have Business enough but the consolation is, that all my proceedings are approv'd of by the Commiss[rs] and Officers here, indeed so far, that they would sooner go by my advice than my Masters which is a dangerous point to keep their good graces and his both, however I will manage it. Amongst the other Officers here the Surgeon to the Yard Mr. Ramsey Ker from the Banks of the Tweed, has more interest than any other, especially with Sir Charles Middleton, Comptroller of the Navy.

This Mr. Ker is my friend, so that if anything happens there is a great probability in the present posture of Affairs that I have a chance by and by to be employ'd as Principal Surveyor, for all the Officers here would greatly prefer it – but these things must come in course. I shall endeavour to secure a proper Basis by performing the duty of my present Station to the satisfaction of all my Superiors.

He found advancement, but also found that work filled almost every hour of the day. He clearly revelled in it, which is as well, for it was to form the pattern for the rest of his life. Social life would always be thrust into second place, and if he ever considered the need for wife and family it was never mentioned. His regime was a punishing one.[6]

> You ask me what I do all winter – I rise in the morning at 7^0 Clock and will continue to get up earlier till it come to 5. I then set seriously to work to make out Acct^s, write on business, or draw till breakfast which is at 9 – next go to breakfast and get into the Yard about Ten. Then all the Officers are in their Offices and if they have anything to say to me or me to them, we do it. This and going round amongst the several Works brings My dinner time, which is about 2^0 Clock; an hour and a half serves this and at half after 3 I again make my appearance when there's generally something wanted and I again go round and see what is going on – and draw till 5 then go to Tea till Six – then I come back to my room and write, draw or read till half after 9 – then comes Supper and Bed Time . . .

He had 'spare time', but it was not to be frittered away.[7]

> Knowledge is my most ardent pursuit, a thousand things occur that would pass unnoticed by good easy people who are contented with trudging on in the beaten Path but I am not contented unless I can reason on every particular. I am now very deep in Chemistry – the manner of making Mortar, led me to enquire into the Nature of Lime &c. in pursuit of this, having look'd in some books on Chemistry I perceived that the field was boundless – and that to assign reasons for many Mechanical processes it required general knowledge of that Science. I have therefore had the loan of a M.S.S. Copy of Dr. Blacks Lectures. I have bought his Experiments on Magnesia and Quick Lime and likewise Fourcroy's Lectures translated from the French by a Mr. Elliott, Edinburgh. And I am determined to study with unwearied attention until I attain some general knowledge of Chemistry as it is of Universal use in the Arts as well as in Medicine. I wish And^w that you saw me at the present instant surrounded by Books, Drawings – Compasses, Pencils and Pens etc. etc. great is the confusion but it pleases my taste and *thats enough.*

An ambitious man, certainly, but one not yet quite sure in what direction that ambition might lead him. It is ironic, given his later career, that in the same letter he joked about the way in which the 'rage for building' was making the wealthy quake as their land was eaten up for public works – 'Canals cut from Sea to Sea: Dreadful Thought!'

Telford remained two years at Portsmouth, surrounded by immense engineering works and construction sites. He was involved with Wyatt in works that he described later as being 'higher class', but more importantly, he was able to see engineering construction with which he had

previously been 'wholly unacquainted'. By 1786, he had amassed considerable experience, become accustomed to taking control of major
works and made a very favourable impression on a number of important men. And he had achieved the latter without recourse to flattery.
He wrote of his relationship with Pulteney:[8]

> His good opinion has always been a great satisfaction to me, and the
> more so, as it has neither been obtained nor preserved by deceit, cring-
> ing, nor flattery; on the contrary, I believe, I am almost the only man who
> speaks out fairly to him, and who contradicts him the most. *We quarrel like
> tinkers.*

He may have climbed on his merits, but without Pulteney he might have
been forced into different paths. As it was, Pulteney offered him the
opportunity of a move away from Portsmouth to Shropshire. He had
recently been elected MP for Shrewsbury, and his estates there included Shrewsbury Castle. The eleventh-century motte and bailey had been
imposed on the community with typical Norman single-mindedness –
over fifty houses were knocked down to make way for it. Over the years
it had been modernised and extended, but was in a run-down, ram-
shackle condition. Nevertheless, Pulteney decided it would make a fit-
ting home for the new Member of Parliament. He asked Telford to take
on the task of renovation. It was true that work on the Commissioner's
House was all but complete, but building work as a whole had certainly not stopped at Portsmouth. Renovating a run-down castle was hardly, in itself, an obviously appealing job for a man who was established as
an important figure in one of the great naval dockyards. One suspects
that the offer came with a very strong hint that Shropshire would have
more to offer in the future. So it was that in 1786, Telford set off to
assume a new role: architect and temporary master of Shrewsbury
Castle.

CHAPTER THREE

The Shropshire Surveyor

Telford had once again arrived at the right place at the right time. It is tempting to say that he was lucky, but it was more than mere fortune: he was also the right man. As each opportunity presented itself for advancement, he had grabbed it and held it firm. To a natural, inbred talent he had added a capacity for unrelenting work. If all we knew of Telford was based on material that survived from his latter years, we would think of him as a somewhat dour character, a workaholic almost totally devoid of social graces. Fortunately, the picture we have of Telford when he arrived at Shrewsbury is very different. Approaching his thirtieth birthday, he was full of good humour, a man of wide-ranging interests. He came to Shropshire seemingly set on establishing himself as an architect, and was soon to have ample opportunity to prove his merits in that profession. He was accepted in his new home town as a professional man and was able to mix freely with the local gentry, although he never made the least attempt to disguise his humble origins. One of the few personal descriptions from this time comes from Katherine Plymley, a member of an important local family, noted for its interests in libertarian causes and particularly heavily involved in the anti-slavery movement. After a visit from Telford, she wrote this appraisal in her diary:[1]

> Mr Telford is a man of highly respect. Born of poor parents in the shire of Dumfries, brought up a common working mason, he has by uncommon genius & by unwearied industry raised himself to be an excellent architect & a most intelligent & enlightened man, his knowledge is general, his conversation very animated, his look full of intelligence &

vivacity. He is eminently chearful & the broad Scotch accent that he retains rather becomes him. He has been settled in Shrewsbury some few years, brought there by Mr Pulteney, who was born in the same parish with him, to make some alterations in the castle since, & has been engaged in many public & private buildings. He is the architect for the new church at Madeley & has just received a very advantageous appointment, the entire management of the canal that is to form a junction between the Severn, Dee and Mersey. But praise of a higher kind belongs to him. What he procures by his merit & industry he bestows most benevolently & liberally: frugal in his own expences, he can do more for others and what he does he does cheerfully.

In this period, as before, poetry remained his first love for his leisure hours, with an enthusiasm that tended towards the morally improving and the informative. He was a devotee of William Cowper's *The Task* – he was certainly not put off by long works; this one runs to six books. It tells a familiar story of the sins of the city spreading to the country, the virtues of honest toil contrasting with the evils of the indolent rich. Cowper's ideal is the honest man who raises himself by his own efforts – a theme which Telford, not surprisingly, approved enthusiastically. Cowper is particularly hard on the village public houses:

> Pass where we may, through city or through town,
> Village or hamlet of this merry land,
> Though lean and beggar'd, ev'ry twentieth pace
> Conducts th' unguarded nose to such a whiff
> Of stale debauch, forth-issuing from the styes
> That law has licens'd, as makes temp'rance reel.
> There sit, involv'd and lost in curling clouds
> Of Indian fume, and guzzling deep, the boor,
> The lackey, and the groom: the craftsman there
> Takes a Lethean leave of all his toil;
> Smith, cobbler, joiner, he that plies the sheers,
> And he that kneads the dough; all loud alike,
> All learned, and all drunk.

This too probably appealed to Telford, who at this time had adopted a very stringent, self-denying diet.[2]

I have myself for about half a year taken to drinking water only, I avoid all sweets, and never eat any nick nacks. I have sowens & Milk every night for my supper. In short Andrew I am a queer creature, and am not ashamed of being thought singular.

It was not a regime he was to continue with for very long.

Another literary enthusiasm was for that most curious of poetic works, Erasmus Darwin's 'The Botanic Garden'. It is a poem glorifying the inventions of the Industrial Revolution, but does so in terms of classical mythology. Nymphs appear to help Savery build his primitive steam engine, and the poem even contains a reasonably accurate account of Arkwright's pioneering machinery for spinning cotton:

> First, with nice eyes, emerging Naiads cull
> From leathery pods the vegetable wool;
> With wiry teeth *revolving cards* release
> The tangled knots, and smooth the ravell'd fleece:
> Next moves the *iron hand* with fingers fine,
> Combs the wire card, and forms th' eternal line;
> Slow with soft lips the *whirling can* acquires
> The tender skeins, and wraps in rising spires:
> With quicken'd pace *successive rollers* move,
> And these retain, and then extend, the *rove*,
> Then fly the spokes, the rapid axles glow,
> While slowly circumvolves the labouring wheel below.

Erasmus Darwin was himself an extraordinarily interesting man, but it is hard to think of his poem as anything other than a curiosity. But one can well understand how its subject matter at least would appeal to a very practical gentleman with a taste for poetry. And, of course, being a Scotsman, Telford inevitably turned to the works of his great contemporary, Robert Burns. Unfortunately, Burns did not share Cowper and Darwin's taste for either moral improvement or machinery. This worried Telford, who thought Burns might be encouraged to write a different kind of verse if only the matter was explained to him clearly: 'attention might perhaps be by this means fixed on those happy, innocent & picturesque views of the manners of the Scottish Peasantry'.[3] The letter was duly sent, and it did not seem to occur to Telford that there was anything remotely incongruous in attempting to persuade Burns, of all people, to write verse aimed at 'preserving the virtuous character' of the young. He also sent copies of his own verses, some of which were in frank imitation of Burns' vernacular style. Sadly, if Burns did reply, there is no evidence of it. Nevertheless, when Burns died in 1796, Telford was moved to produce some of the best poetry he ever wrote, in which, for once, the polite stanzas of conventional verse give way before a sense of genuine grief and vehement feeling.

> The Muses shall that fatal hour
> To Lethe's streams consign,

Which gave the little slaves of pow'r
To scoff at worth like thine

But thy fair fame shall rise and spread
Thy name be dear to all;
When down to their oblivious bed,
Official insects fall.

So he could produce work of quality, but as he himself admitted, the trouble was that most of the time he wrote as a recreation, and could seldom find the time – or perhaps the inclination – for revisions. He called his writings 'word frittering'.

At Shrewsbury, in the early years, he actually seemed to have had some spare time for amusement. He delighted in a comic performance by a London actress; went to the races just once – 'I care nothing for them' – and ventured into the world of music. He was the first to admit an ignorance of music and went off to a concert with little hope of enjoying anything apart from the songs – 'If they let me hear the Words I'll tell you what I think of the matter'. His prognosis proved all too accurate.[4]

> Now I have been at the Concert, and I might as well have staid at home – It was all very fine, I have no doubt, but I would not give a Song of Jock Stewart for the whole … It is certainly a defect – but it is certainly a fact – I have no enjoyment from fine Music. I sit down and am as attentive as any mortal can be, nay endeavour to interest my feelings but all in vain. I feel no emotion unless an inclination to sleep be reckoned upon.

From his taste in poetry, we know that Telford was very much a liberal in his outlook, but it is rare that we find a hint of any great interest in the political issues of the day. When Little raised the topic, he pleaded ignorance:[5]

> With regard to politics you shall have it all your own way – for I will freely confess that I know nothing of the matter, and am therefore unfit to give an opinion for I am so totally enveloped in my own business that I very seldom read a paper – indeed for half a year past I have scarcely had time.

Yet, in 1791, he wrote a long letter expressing opinions which are perhaps very much what one would expect. He had read Tom Paine – as perhaps every literate person in Britain had at that time – and while he could not countenance revolution, he clearly saw the need for social change. And why would he not? His world was one where rapid change was accepted as the norm. One of the leading figures of the day, now remembered chiefly as a chemist who first isolated the element oxygen, was Joseph Priestley. He counted leading industrialists and engineers among his closest friends, including Boulton and Watt and Josiah Wedgwood. He was also radical in his politics, and was said to have attended a Bastille Day dinner. The country was in the middle of an anti-French ferment and anyone seen as pro-revolutionary could incur the fury of the mob in what became known as the 'Church and King' riots. Priestley was doubly qualified; a non-conformist, he was seen as opposing the established Church, and the mere rumour, which turned out to be untrue, that he had attended the infamous dinner declared him to be anti-king. His house was stormed and he was forced to flee for his life. This is the background against which Telford wrote one of his most thoughtful letters, and for that reason alone it is worth quoting at length.[6]

It appears that Mr Paines Pamphlet has had its full effect upon the Langholm Patriots, tho' you do not tell us who were so warm in the cause of Liberty – I hope it will not operate to excess. Steady resolution founded on th upon thoro' examination and firm conviction is much to be preferred to the violent ebullitions of enraged Passions, we may seriously rejoice at the welfare of our neighbours and anxiously desire a reformation at home, but we should carefully avoid any tendency to excess or anarchy for they are too frequently the attendants of popular reformations.

Since my last I have read a vindication of the Revolution in France by a James Mackintosh Esqr which is reckn'd the best of any that has yet been published on that subject it is certainly much better wrote than Paine, when I say better wrote, I mean that he treats the several parts more methodically, he goes deeper into and manages the arguments with great greater nicety, his language is more refin'd, and he has still animated the whole subject with a due proportion of the glowing Spirit of Patriotism. Yet I am persuaded that Paines manner is better calculated to work upon the general mass of Mankind, his rough Sketches are the bold dashes of a masterly hand, he strongly marks the leading features while the fire of enthusiasm will not permit him to fill up a finish'd picture, but his picture is such as fully to rouse the attention, and fill the whole Soul with indignation against the System of Despotism and all its appendages.

I am convinced that the situation of Great Britain, tho' perhaps not quite so alarming as he represents is yet such that nothing short of some signal revolution can prevent her from sinking into Bankruptcy, Slavery and Insignificancy our pecuniary embarrassments are so perplexing, our statesmen are so fond of power the pernicious system of continental connections, is so prevalent, while the influence of distant colonisation is so necessary to the support of corrupt administration, that little change is to be expected from the ordinary course of Government. It would require the united abilities, integrity and independence of a hundred *Pulteneys* to purge the bloated mass and restore it to health and Vigour. And that alas! can never be expected ...

You will before this arrives, have had an account of the destruction made by the Birmingham Riotous Mob; the following are the Heads, the Revolution Gentlemen, met according to their appointment and dined at a Hotel, Dr Priestly did not attend. there was a Mr Ker in the Chair they din'd and drank a few toasts which are now published, the first was the King and Constitution, they parted a little after 6^0 clock and each went quietly to his own habitation. The evening before, a Handbill of a seditious leniency was thrown into shops and otherwise dispersed, this, on the next day was attributed to Dr Priestly tho' he has publickly disavowed knowing of any such thing, and it is confidently reported to have been fabricated and circulated by some leading people who bore him a grudge. However it was, the Mob was somehow or other inflam'd. They assembled in great numbers, they marched to the Hotel where the Gentlemen dined, but who were then gone. They demanded Dr Priestly and not finding him there they broke the Windows of the Hotel, they next proceeded to and deliberately destroy'd two meeting Houses at the same time keeping Engines playing upon the Houses of each. And after having performed this they marched in triumph to the house of Dr Priestly, which was about a mile and a half from the Town, but before they arrived some kind friend had just time to inform the D^r of his danger, and to convey him his Wife and Daughter away in a carriage. the D^r says 'They with difficulty made their escape with the Clothes they had on, no more'. The vile dregs of mankind immediately arrived, and in a little while the Drs Philosophical apparatus his valuable manuscripts and every part of his Household furniture, fell a sacrifice to their implacable fury they afterwards proceeded to and destroy'd most of the houses of the principal Dissenters in and about Birmingham.

He added a P.S. – 'I cannot help observing that Presbyterianism seems to be the only Religion of Liberty'.

The portrait that emerges at this time is of a good-humoured man who had made his own way in the world and was not disposed to disguise the fact. His interest in some of the arts was clearly strong and genuine, but where he felt himself unmoved he found no reason to pretend an interest. His politics were liberal and humanitarian, but he never actively engaged with any political parties. But what of his personal and professional ambitions? He presented himself to the world first and foremost as an architect, but already circumstances were conspiring to move him in new directions.

As work went on with the restoration of the castle, the big opportunity arose that could well have been the carrot that brought him to Shrewsbury. He was appointed county surveyor. This was one of those rather nebulous posts that could involve a great deal or hardly anything. The local justices were responsible for public buildings and the upkeep of the highways. Some counties spent nothing on public buildings and considered they had fulfilled their obligations for highway maintenance by instructing someone with a wheelbarrow to shovel dirt into the more obvious potholes. Others took their obligations more seriously, and Shropshire was one of these. As a result, their surveyor could expect to find himself in control of some very important projects. It is no wonder that Telford could scarcely contain his enthusiasm at the prospect opening up before him.[7]

> Mr. Pulteney has been gone a fortnight and I am again commanding officer in this renowned fortress, and from which I lay the Town and County under Contribution in every direction – (only in the building line) and as this is a kind of Metropolis to Wales, it naturally falls under my jurisdiction. I have not yet made any attempts in that quarter, nor do I know what will be the consequence, but having now secured a Majority, nay I hope nearly a nem. con. in the rich County of Salop, you will not be surprised if some projects should enter my brain in order to extend the scene of action. The Gentlemen having once interested themselves and publickly declared their opinion, it becomes their own act and rebounds to their honour, to render their Surveyor respectable, and on my part it requires a continual something to keep the spirit awake. This has hitherto luckily been the case, and I think there's a chance for its increasing.

By early 1787, Telford was clearly making his mark in the town. He was buzzing with ideas for improvements of all kinds: 'I have drawn 5 or 6 plans for different alterations at and above the Castle. I have made a Survey and Plan of part of the High Street of Salop and last session a vote was made to sweep away the half of one side, on purpose to render it a good and open Street'. And his new position also brought him private clients, one of whom wanted a whole square designed and the second a country house costing a thousand pounds, a point which greatly impressed Telford, who heavily underlined the word 'thousand' in his letter.[8]

The most important public buildings that came under his control were a new gaol and an infirmary. The original plans for the gaol had been prepared by J. H. Haycock, but before work was begun, Telford had the chance to discuss them with one of the great men of the age, the prison reformer: John Howard. Howard was on one of his regular tours of inspection, and Telford made the most of the opportunity to meet a man whom he admired enormously and to discuss the two new buildings. The meeting was a great success. The two men formed an instant rapport and Telford received just the impetus he needed to refashion the plans and make them his own.[9]

> About 10 days ago, I had a visit from the celebrated John Howard, Esq. – I say *I* for he was on his tour to Jails & Infirmarys and they being both under my direction, of course was the cause of being thus distinguished I accompanied him to the Infirmary & the Jail. I shewed him the plans of both and had much conversation with him on these subjects – in consequence of his observations on the former I have made a plan for a thorough reformation, which has been approved at a general Board, and is now referred to a Committee – his remarks on the latter I on Saturday lay before a general meeting of the Commissioners, and very probably shall have the new modelling their plan of that large building, as he has found several faults – you will easily conceive how I enjoyed the conversation of this truly good man – and with what attention I would court his good opinion, I considered him as the guardian Angel of the miserable & distressed, travelling over the world, merely for the sake of doing good, shunning the society of men, and afraid of being taken notice of.

It was not just the professional advice that impressed Telford; he was even more taken with the man himself. Howard did not enjoy either the travel or his fame, and would have infinitely preferred to sit quietly at home, but his sense of moral duty drove him on. His travels were to take him to the shores of the Black Sea, where he died of fever in 1790. The prison still shows something of the humanitarian views that Telford and Howard shared. The main building has a certain elegance, and even the rather forbidding stone entrance is lightened by a niche under the broken pediment, containing a bust of Howard.

One other result of Howard's visit was a proposal that convicts would be better employed in useful work rather than sitting in their cells thinking over their grievances. Telford used them as labourers, most interestingly in excavating the Roman remains at Wroxeter. This was Virconium, once the fourth largest city in Britain. It began as a legionary fortress in the first century AD, then developed into a major market centre. The most impressive remains are those of the public baths originally at the centre of Virconium. Archaeology was not new – the Society of Antiquaries had been founded in London in 1707 – but huge-scale excavations were still rare. The early work was crude, but it did at least establish the importance of sites and put a stop, often very belatedly, to the practice of considering them as convenient sources for building stone. Anyone travelling through the countryside near Hadrian's Wall will have no difficulty spotting well-squared Roman stone blocks in many of the older farms and houses. The idea of excavation had an obvious appeal to Telford. The classical revival was still very much in vogue, and his two early mentors, Chambers and Adam, had studied in Rome. There was no possibility of Telford visiting Italy, but he could at least study a small part of the great Roman Empire almost in his own backyard, on the Pulteney estates. What Telford observed was the way in which local farmers discerned the presence of stone under their land by noticing crop marks: the way in which corn grows differently when there is a huge amount of stone just below the surface, a phenomenon still used to identify sites through aerial photography. At Wroxeter they had discovered a tiled floor and pillars, and Telford and his convicts set out to remove the top soil. It was scarcely scientific work, but with Pulteney's enthusiastic backing, a great deal was discovered. The site was correctly identified as a large bath house, which Telford described as consisting of a dressing room, a cold bath, a hot bath and a 'sudetorium' or sweat room. In fact, the site is more complex than he realised, with a series of baths ranging from very hot through tepid to cold plunge pools, and there was even an open-air swimming pool. A great deal of new excavation has revealed the full extent of the site, but if Pulteney had not enthused his friend and surveyor, much more might have ended up in local barns and pig sties.

County surveyors were not always well qualified for the work and many took the job as a mere sinecure. Consequently, they were not always highly regarded by the locals. In 1788, Telford was called in to look at the possibility of repairing the roof of the church of St Chad in Shrewsbury. Rain was coming in through the roof, but what struck Telford were the alarmingly large cracks in the wall. He duly reported to the church wardens that there was no point in doing anything about the roof until the walls were repaired – and, in his opinion, if the walls were not repaired pretty quickly they would have no roof to worry about. His views were treated with derision.[10]

These fractures were said to have been there time immorial – and it was said by even sensible people that Professional men always wish'd to carve out employment for themselves: and that the whole might be done at a small expense which they proceeded to do – and I gave myself no disturbance when lo: & behold on the Morning of the 9th inst the very parts I had pointed out, gave way – and down tumbled the mighty mass – forming a very remarkable, magnificent Ruin, while astonished and surprised the inhabitants were roused from their delirium – *tho' they have not yet recovered from the shock.*

In the event, it seems unlikely that any remedial work could have saved the church, but the dramatic collapse did wonders for Telford's reputation. Over the next few years he had the chance to design two churches in the county, at Bridgnorth and Madeley. The latter is somewhat dour, octagonal in plan, with a squat, square tower. The detail on the outside is dull, with plain windows lighting the nave, and taller, round-headed windows above them at the level of the gallery. Bridgnorth is more imaginative and satisfactory. At Madeley he had all the freedom of an open site, but at Bridgnorth he had severe restraints and, as he recognised, a location where creating a good effect mattered a great deal: 'The Entrance End of the new Church is to front & nearly fill the end of one of the principal streets and one side is to show itself to the lower Town and adjacent County – the Tower & Cupola will be seen in all directions'.[11]

The most impressive view is certainly that along East Castle Street, which the church does indeed close off at one end. There is a bold front with a wide pediment, above which a well-proportioned tower rises in three stages, topped by a dome. The sides have round-headed windows, as at Madeley, but here they rise to almost the full height of the building between pilasters, creating a pleasing light effect. Telford would never have been a great architect, but he was a competent designer working with the accepted styles of his time. The two churches are the most important works of this kind that he ever designed, but neither shows the least hint of originality. His genius lay elsewhere, and it was just at this time that it first came to light.

The River Severn is one of the dominant features in the Shropshire landscape, and was to provide a recurring theme throughout Telford's life. The first bridge that was entirely his own design crossed the river at Montford, to the west of Shrewsbury. It still stands, though it has been widened to take new walkways, and carries the traffic of the busy A5. It shows a very practical stonemason's eye, and everything was

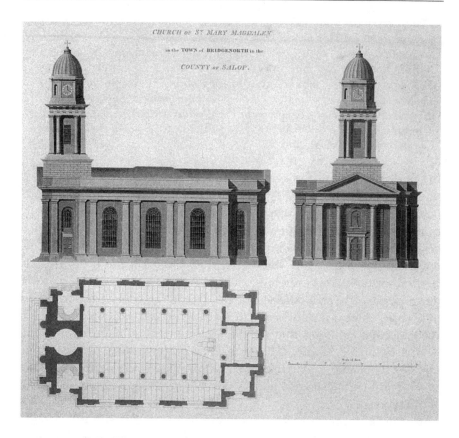

Telford's coolly classical design for St Mary's Church, Bridgnorth.

designed to make the job of construction as simple as possible. The line of the road crosses the river at an angle, but Telford was not interested in complex skew arches; it is, of course, perfectly possible that he was unsure how to construct one. So the bridge was built at right angles to the banks, and the road had to go into sharp bends at either end to accommodate it. The river is crossed by three sandstone arches – 58 feet (17.7 metres) in the centre and 50 feet (15.2 metres) to either side. The prominent voussoirs round the three arches are finished at right angles to simplify the laying of the stone courses of the spandrels. The whole thing is very workmanlike, and the basic simplicity might be partly explained by the fact that, once again, convicts were used as a labour force, with expertise provided by two local contractors. Nevertheless, this was Telford's first big work of this kind, and it was very important to him that all went well. He needed someone on site on whom he could absolutely rely, and he turned at once to his Eskdale connections. He had already been instrumental in using his Pulteney contacts to get his old friend and former colleague Matthew Davidson work at Bath. Now, he sent for him to come to Shropshire to supervise work on the bridge, which was to prove the starting point of a working relationship to last for the rest of Davidson's life. He was a curious, cantankerous character. Whereas Telford never lost his pride in, nor his love for, his native country, Davidson seldom had a good word to say for Scotland. Yet the two men remained friends as well as collaborators in great works for, whatever Davidson's faults, he satisfied the one condition that was of supreme importance: he knew his trade, he could be relied upon. All went well at the bridge, an entirely conventional construction. Good stone was available near the site at Nesscliffe, and the work itself used the usual technique of building up the foundations behind the protection of coffer dams. Over the next thirty years, Telford was to be responsible for five more major bridges over the Severn, all of them either grander or more innovative than this first modest structure.

At the beginning of 1793, he still seems to have had his sights firmly set on a career as an architect, and he set off for a journey via Gloucester to visit the city that was setting new architectural ideals for Britain: Bath.[12] His journey took him down through the prosperous valleys centred on Stroud, where woollen mills new and old lined every stream and river. He was as enthusiastic about the beauty of these Cotswold valleys as he was about the wealth they were so obviously enjoying. He mused over the people, and wondered whether they would prove as good-natured and comfortable as their surroundings. They were to prove a sad disappointment. He once arrived at an ale-house, where he found a drunken rabble – led by an equally intoxicated landlord – ranting 'Church and King' sentiments, not likely to please Telford. Into this noisy scene stepped a poor German Jew, looking for work in the local mills. He was immediately assumed to be a French spy, one foreigner being much the same as another. His explanations did nothing to improve the situation, for when he asked for food the jolly landlord proceeded to try and force him to eat a vast hunk of ham. The thought of eating ham was even more distressing for the poor man than being mistaken for a spy, and what the outcome would have been if Telford had not stepped in is not difficult to imagine. It says a good deal for his personality that he was able to pacify the landlord and the drunks, and at the same time buy bread and cheese for 'poor little Moss', sending him on his way if not content, then at least well fed.

Bath had been developed in the early part of the eighteenth century, largely thanks to three men, at least as far as the buildings were concerned: Ralph Allen, who provided the beautiful Bath stone from his quarries, a stone whose honeyed warmth adds much to the charm of the city; and the architects John Wood, father and son – not one man, as Telford appears to have thought. The Woods gave Bath its two grand promenades, the first of their kind in England, Grand Parade and North Parade, and two of the supreme examples of Georgian architecture, The Circus and Royal Crescent. Telford viewed these with enthusiasm, but by the time of his visit, the huge popularity of Bath with the fashionable world had led to an onrush of speculative building, which he viewed with disgust.

> I think I have told you that Modern Bath has been created by a Mr. Wood, an Architect, a man of very superior talents to whom, if I will, I hope to do justice. Since his time, altho' the rage for Building has been unbounded, yet there has none inherited even a portion of his Genius. I will not even except their present Surveyor who is sinking fast into oblivion. He has lost, or rather not succeeded, in the finest attempt which the World ever afforded for finding his fame above that of any other man as an Architect ... In the late improvements of the old Town the same hand is blundering round about a meaning tho' he might have far excell'd the Bath of Dioclesian or any of the Roman Works.

This is one of the few letters that gives us a chance to judge Telford's architectural taste, and it is quite clear that he was not afraid to form an opinion and express it boldly, and most contemporary architectural commentators would agree with his verdict. He was perhaps a little unkind to John Palmer, the city surveyor, who had only taken office in 1792, and one cannot always have the services of architects of genius. He also had the sense to realise that the pressure for development was the driving force and that standards had been allowed to slip in the demands of speed and profit. Today, we can perhaps take a more lenient view, since we have seen the horrors of the 1960s and 1970s, when Bath's planners allowed lumpen blocks, including a monumentally ugly multi-storey car park, to be dropped down in the very heart of the city.

From Bath, Telford proceeded to London, avoiding the highwaymen and footpads – 'The Collectors' as he called them – who ranged across

Hounslow Heath. In London he had a chance to study both architectural books and works, and then moved on to Oxford, which delighted him. He admired the paintings in Christ Church, though his comments suggest that he was more overwhelmed by subject matter than painting qualities: Rubens's *Medusa* made him shudder and he felt that the painter 'must have had a long handle to his brush', while Caracci's painting of his family showed them as a 'fine set of blackguards'. Although he admired the old university colleges, 'the Gothic' was of less interest than the modern additions. He noted that 'twas here that Sr. Christ. Wren first tryed his architectural skill'. This is the Sheldonian Theatre, built not for performances but for ceremonials, and still one of Oxford's gems. It was Wren's first building in as much as it was the first to be started, though not the first to be completed – and it is certainly not his best work, though it has a good deal of charm. Had he had a chance to view it in detail, Telford would surely have appreciated the ingenuity Wren showed in throwing a huge roof over an area of 70 by 80 feet (21 by 24 metres). But his greatest praise was reserved for the now all but forgotten Dr Henry Aldrich of Christ Church, precisely because his work exemplified the current enthusiasm for neo-classicism which he himself shared. From Oxford, he travelled to Birmingham, which he scornfully dismissed as 'famous for *Buttons, Buckles* and *Locks* and *Ignorance* and *Barbarism*'. The treatment of Priestley by the mob was neither forgotten nor forgiven. He had in fact only visited this sink of iniquity in order to see the stained-glass designer who was to work on the Madeley windows. Afterwards, he returned to Shropshire, having enjoyed what was for him the very rare experience of travelling for a purpose other than work.

This period of his life was in many ways a happy one. He was enjoying having a position of authority: 'I have been very busy lately for the Quarter Sessions which were over yesterday, but however I carried every point I wanted, tho' I was obliged to speak a good deal, and even bully a little – some of these fellows are ignorant and obstinate'.[13] It was not presumably a view which he made too obvious to the Bench of Justices, though he declared himself on good terms with 'the sensible part'. He had works of importance under his control and could indulge his taste for architecture. To many men it would have seemed a comfortable and satisfying life, but there was a daemon at work in Thomas Telford that would not settle for anything quite so simple. He only communicated his true self to Andrew Little.[14]

To tell you the truth to set my mother and you above the fear of want has always been my first object, altho' I never have told you so before – and next to that, to be that somebody that you have always taught me to believe I had a right to. and I humbly presume that there is a something in it – it may be self-confidence, but I think that I have observed that there has always been a bustle where I was – how that came about I know not, or whether it is true, I know not – but these are the simple facts. You know while I was in Eskdale I was a bone of contention, when I came to London I had nearly raised a confusion at Somerset House – at Portsmo' the navy Bd & Adm^lty were engaged, and since my arrival here, there has been one continual scene of contention, where I have always been the prominent feature. What will be the consequence I know not.

What the problem was in Eskdale is simply not known, but there is more than a hint here that ambition was strong in the man, and that he was by no means averse to upsetting others in pursuit of his own ends. Just how strong that side of his character was has become a matter of some debate, in particular with regard to the events of the next few years, for his life was about to go through yet another major change that was to set it on a new track, there to remain until his death.

CHAPTER FOUR

The First Canals

The canal age appeared as a natural development, following a long period when river navigation had been steadily improved. A point was reached where further improvement could only be achieved by the creation of wholly artificial waterways that would extend navigation to the new, rapidly developing industrial centres of Birmingham and Manchester. Enthusiasm for canals grew rapidly, largely thanks to the immense success of the Bridgewater Canal both as a piece of engineering and, just as importantly, a money-making venture. Opened in 1761, linking the Duke of Bridgewater's mines at Worsley to Manchester, it caught the public imagination, and for a time the aqueduct at Barton was the wonder of the age. Of the two men largely responsible for the engineering, John Gilbert was committed to the duke's many interests and so it was left to the second innovator, James Brindley, to dominate the first wave of canal building. The boom time ended with the American War of Independence, and there was a lengthy period of recovery before the next surge of canal construction began. When it resumed, it did so with a vengeance, to such an extent that the years from 1792 to 1794 became known as the years of 'canal mania'. In that period, no fewer than thirty-nine new canals were authorised, as well as numerous improvements to existing waterways. By now, Brindley was dead, and a new engineer carried the brunt of the mania years. William Jessop was to have an immense influence on Telford's career, while the relationship between the two remains a matter of controversy and debate. No true picture of the next stage of Telford's life and career can be painted without reference to Jessop and his influence.

William Jessop was born in 1745 at Plymouth, the son of a foreman shipwright. The elder Jessop became involved with work on the Eddystone lighthouse under the direction of the greatest civil engineer of the day, John Smeaton. As a result, fourteen-year-old William was taken on as an apprentice to the great man, and it is difficult to imagine a better start for anyone with ambitions for a career in civil engineering. Smeaton was involved in river navigation work and was engineer to two very important waterways, the Calder & Hebble and the Forth & Clyde Canals. Young Jessop worked steadily and diligently, so that by the time the canal mania years had begun, there was scarcely an engineer in the country with as much experience or such an excellent reputation. His services were hugely in demand, and by 1793, he had accepted the position of chief engineer on some of the most demanding projects of the eighteenth century. The most important was undoubtedly the Grand Junction Canal, offering a direct link between London and Birmingham. The most difficult was the Rochdale Canal, thrusting through the heart of the Pennines to form a link between his old master's waterway, the Calder & Hebble, and Manchester. The now largely forgotten Barnsley Canal also provided an important link between the South Yorkshire coalfield and numerous industrial centres. Besides these was a canal which was not particularly significant in terms of the waterways network as a whole, but which was destined to provide the greatest engineering challenge of them all: the Ellesmere Canal.

Proposals were put forward as early as 1789 for a canal that would link three rivers, the Dee, the Mersey and the Severn, as well as reaching the coal mines and ironworks of North Wales. Several rival schemes were advanced, and in 1791, Jessop was asked to consider the best route. He found it impossible to reconcile all the interests, and his eventual proposal was for a canal that would link the existing Chester Canal, running between Chester and Nantwich, with the ironworks beyond the Dee, near Llangollen. It was this line that was approved by an Act of Parliament in April 1793. Even then, not all the details had been worked out and there were some difficult problems to solve.

Those travelling the Ellesmere Canal today, popularly known as the Llangollen, may not be aware of just how well it was planned. Jessop was able to use his considerable experience to good effect. The canal rises steeply from the Cheshire Plain by a flight of locks before setting off on the journey into Wales. In places, it follows the natural contours of the land, avoiding unnecessary earthworks; in other areas, it slices ruthlessly through the landscape in deep cuttings or climbs high above it on tall embankments. But this was only one of Jessop's many commitments and not the most important. It was perfectly clear that while he could be in overall control, and would take all the important decisions as to where and how the canal was to be built, there was absolutely no possibility of his being able to oversee the whole works on a day-to-day basis.

Jessop had three assistants working for him who had all been involved in the planning stage of the Ellesmere Canal, and one of these, William Turner, was quite confident of getting the post of resident engineer. But the committee who controlled the canal company had other ideas. Without consulting Jessop, they wrote to their own man, Thomas Telford, offering him the position. Telford was of course delighted and passed the news on to Little that he was at the heart of yet another bustle.[1]

> Last Monday I was appointed Sole Agent, Architect and Engineer to the Canal which is to join the Mersey and Dee and the Severn. It is the greatest work I believe, that is now in hand, in this kingdom, and will not be completed for many years to come. You will be surprised that I have not mentioned this to you before, but the fact is that I had no idea of any such thing untill an application was made to me from some of the leading Gentlemen, and I was appointed at their meeting, tho many others had made much interest for the place. I cannot be said to be confirmed until after the general assembly of the Proprietors which is to be held on the 31 Octr. tho' 'tis not likely that that meeting will do away with the act of a numerous Committee of the leading Men. This is a great and laborious undertaking but the line which it opens is vast and noble, and coming in this honourable way I thought it too great an opportunity to be neglected. Mr. Pulteney approves much of it, as do all my friends. it will require great exertions but it is worthy of them all, there is a very great Aqueduct over the Dee, besides Bridges over several Rivers, which cross the line of March.

Now, this letter is particularly interesting. It is, to say the least, disingenuous. Clearly Telford, with his well-established connections, must have known exactly what was going on in his own patch, and as we have already seen he had become an adept manipulator of influential men in a position to further his cause. His letter actually predates the announcement that the job was becoming available, so a good deal of back-door diplomacy must have been involved. He was not a natural candidate for the job. Up to that point, his principal experience had been as an architect and there is no evidence of his knowing anything about canal engineering. All that could be said was that he had shown himself adept at bridge and road construction. He was most certainly not the first choice of the man in charge of the project – indeed, Jessop had not even considered him at all. William Turner was not surprisingly aggrieved and complained to Jessop, who wrote a very frank reply.[2]

> I have your letter and feel myself under some difficulty in answering it; because I am uninformed of the motives which have directed the resolves of the Committee. I think as you do that no one Man can properly undertake the actual direction of the whole of so extensive a concern as a Man of Art; and at the same time manage the Accompts.
>
> I have always advised every person who was engaged in the direction of the Mechanical part of a Business of this kind not to divide his attention by interfering as an Accomptant because he may have full employment in the former if he makes the best use of his time; and others better qualified for the latter than he probably can be may have full employment also; I am quite unacquainted with Mr. Telford and with his Character; from the little acquaintance I have had with you I wish you might have the direction of that part of the Business which you have proposed to undertake and I do not think the Terms you have offered to undertake it for are unreasonable – if the Committee should consult me on this question I should tell them so, but I cannot be at the next General Meeting any that I may see or hear from in the mean time shall know my Opinion on this head and you may make such use of this Letter as you may think proper.

He could hardly have been plainer, but the committee declined to take the advice of their highly experienced engineer and confirmed Telford in the appointment. Would there have been a different result had Jessop been able to go to the meeting? The question is unanswerable. Telford described the events.[3]

> I duly received yours of the 6th Oct. but agreeable to your request I deferred answering it untill I could let you know the determination of the general meeting of the Ellesmere Canal Navigation, which was held last Wednesday. They have confirmed my appointment as general Agent. I have reserved the right to carry on such of my architectural business as does not require my personal attendance, so that I shall retain all I wish for of that, which are the Public Buildings and Houses of importance. The other parts of our business are better to be without: they give a great deal of unpleasant labour for very little profit in short they are like the calls of a Country Surgeon. These I shall give up without reluctance, except what relates to Mr. Pulteney and Lady Bath and I have the plea-

sure to say that they are not disposed to quit me. You will not be surprised that altho this employment was offered to me, that there should be many who looked forward to it with anxious eyes and that they had endeavoured to raise a party at the general meeting, but we were too powerful for opposition. I am fortunate in being on good terms with most of the leading men whether of property or abilities and on this occasion I had the decided support of the great John Wilkinson, king of the Iron Masters, who is in himself an host. I travelled in his Carriage to the Meeting found him much disposed to be friendly.

The letter rings true, though one might quibble with the 'party raised against me', since we can now see it more as a party raised in favour of a more highly qualified man. It does make it clear just how much local influence was used to sway the judgement. It is also clear that, however much he prized the new position, he had not quite given up his old, architectural ambitions, or at any rate was keeping his options open. If Telford was an unknown quantity to Jessop, so the world of canals was not yet understood by Telford. It was not very long, however, before he came to realise that he had finally, at the age of thirty-six, found his true vocation.

Telford was given the grand title of 'General Agent, Surveyor, Engineer, Architect and Overlooker to the Ellesmere Canal', and at the very respectable salary of £500 per annum, out of which he was expected to pay the wages of a clerk and an assistant. Fortune certainly favoured Telford. If discussions over the route had not been so protracted, the canal would have begun without his involvement. As his letters indicate, there were still decisions to be taken, and what he could not have known beforehand was that this waterway was to contain the most spectacular engineering achievement of the whole canal age, and that his involvement with it was to help cement his enduring reputation.

As business got under way, Telford was called upon to find himself an assistant, not a difficult decision to take, for he needed a man who was not only of proven worth, but could be relied upon to remain unswervingly loyal. Telford was only too aware that he had won his place as much by influence as by merit, and was concerned that factions would continue to oppose him. He called on Matthew Davidson.[4]

Davidson is canal mad, and there will now be occasions for all his exertions, for beside the real labour that attends such a great public work, Contentions, jealousies and prejudices are stationed like gloomy sentinels from one extremity of the Line to the other. But as I have heard my mother say, that an honest man might look the Devil in the face without being afraid, we must trudge on in the old way.

Although Telford was unfamiliar with some aspects of canal construction, many of the techniques would have been familiar from his work on the Shropshire road system, from taking levels to building simple bridges. One alarming problem facing the canal engineers was the crossing of Whixall Moss, an area of black, oozy peat bogs interspersed with small lakes, or meres. Happily, Jessop had considerable experience of land drainage, ranging from the fens of East Anglia to the Somerset Levels. The first straight cut through the bog acted as a drain, and as the land began to dry out, a bank was built up in which the navigable canal could be set. Telford was to learn a great deal about civil engineering during his time with the Ellesmere. The biggest problems, however, lay at the western end. To reach the extensive ironworks centred on Ruabon, the canal would have to cross the valley of the River Ceiriog, cover 2 miles of ground with a considerable rise in the centre, before crossing the even deeper and wider valley of the Dee. Of the two crossings, the Dee was by far the more difficult.

Various proposals were put forward involving aqueducts of different lengths. The obvious solution would seem to be an aqueduct simply spanning the valley, but there was a question of level. If the canal had been brought along at a natural level, the aqueduct would have needed to rise to a height of over 100 feet and be some 2500 feet long. Nothing of this scale had ever been attempted, but a drawing exists of a design, built in the Roman manner, with a double tier of arches. It would certainly have had the necessary strength, but materials and labour would have made it prohibitively expensive. A more sensible solution was initially adopted: dropping the canal on either side of the valley by locks, thereby reducing the height and length of the proposed aqueduct. But as this would have acted as a sump, there would have needed to be a system for pumping water back up to the higher levels of the canal. The site was Pontcysyllte and the aqueduct was to be carried on three arches. Even at this reduced scale, it would have been the largest structure of its kind in Britain. Telford, the new boy, was presented with a design prepared by the disappointed William Turner and told to produce detailed specifications, sections and working drawings so that an estimate could be prepared and the work advertised for contractors to put in their bids. Not surprisingly, Telford had to report two weeks later that he was not yet ready.[5]

Mr Telford having stated to this Committee that he is not sufficiently prepared to enable him to advertize the proposals for erecting the Aqueduct
at Pontcysyltee And that he wishes to consult Mr Jessop upon various
points relating to it It is Ordered that the advertizement be postponed
until such time as Mr Telford shall have consulted Mr Jessop upon the
Subject And that Mr Telford have Credit on Messrs Eyton and Company
the Bankers for One hundred pounds to enable him to prosecute the
said work at Pontcysylltee.

It was to be two months later, at the end of March, before everything
was complete and the advertisement could be placed. As this was the
most important work on the canal, Matthew Davidson was despatched
to the Dee valley to take the day-to-day responsibility for the works. It
would have been out of character for Telford simply to have accepted
another engineer's view of the best way of building the aqueduct, and
it seems that he was already toying with other notions. A drawing exists,
signed and dated by Telford, for an iron aqueduct on trussed girders,
supported by iron trestle piers. It has been suggested that this might
have been a design for Pontcysyllte, but it seems more likely that it represents nothing more than Telford trying out ideas on paper, with no
intention of advancing them as practical solutions to the problem. If
built, it would certainly have been a most interesting, not to say alarming, structure. In the meantime, work went ahead on preparing foundations for the stone piers of a conventional aqueduct.

After little more than a year on the Ellesmere, Telford found himself
suddenly elevated to the post of chief engineer on another canal. Josiah
Clowes had been appointed chief engineer of the Shrewsbury Canal,
and work was well advanced when he died unexpectedly. This was the
canal that Telford was to see through to completion. He could simply
have followed the lines set out by his able predecessor, but that was not
his way. The canal was a comparatively modest affair, just 18 miles long,
linking Shrewsbury to the Ketley Canal and the old Shropshire Canal.
This area of Shropshire was notable for its innovations, notably the
Ketley inclined plane in which a tub boat floated into a lock, and as the
water was let out, the boat settled onto a wooden carriage set on a sloping railed track. It descended to a lower level of the canal, and as the
cargo was all downhill from the ironworks at the upper level, the weight
of the descending boat could be used to haul up an empty boat on parallel tracks. Telford knew the system well and later described its workings
in detail in one of his few published works.[6] The important point is that
this innovative scheme was the work of the local iron master, William

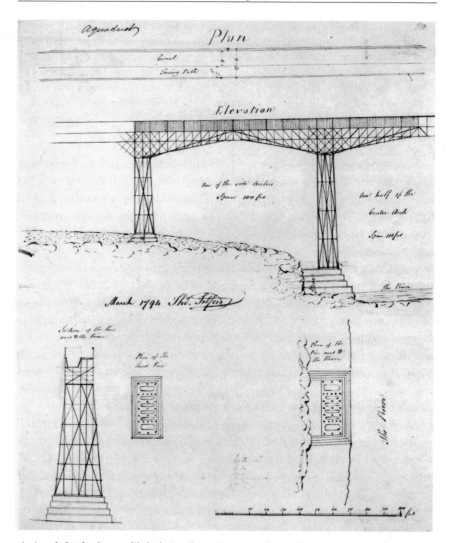

A signed sketch of an unlikely design for an iron trough aqueduct, at one time thought of as an early suggestion for Pontcysyllte.

Reynolds. He was unusual among the industrialists of his day in that he was an enthusiastic scientist. He read all the leading journals of the day in both French and English and had a laboratory built at his home. His experiments were to lead to a patent for making manganese steel, far ahead of its time in terms of application. He took a keen interest in the Shrewsbury Canal and it was inevitable that he and Telford would prove enthusiastic collaborators in finding new solutions to old problems.

Work on the canal was already well advanced and already included some unusual features, notably the 'guillotine' locks in which the gates fell and rose vertically, counterbalanced rather crudely by boxes filled with stones. One important structure, however, remained to be completed: the aqueduct over the River Tern at Longdon. Clowes had designed a wholly conventional masonry aqueduct, which would have been entirely suitable for the job. The river was not navigable, so the whole structure could be carried on low arches. There would have been no justification for changing the plan if flood water had not carried away the original, partially built arches. Now, as we have seen, Telford had already been envisaging cast-iron aqueducts, and here he had an enthusiastic ally. It was clearly in Reynolds's interest to develop new uses for iron, particularly in building and construction works. There had been a splendid start with the famous Darby bridge of 1779, which gave the town of Ironbridge its name, but there had been little in the way of development in the structural use of cast iron. Reynolds was not alone. Benjamin Outram was at the same time planning a modest cast-iron aqueduct on the Derby Canal. So here we have Reynolds and Telford planning an iron trough aqueduct at Longdon and Outram planning another at Derby. Significantly, Outram had a partner at his Butterley ironworks – William Jessop. Historians tend to worry about who should get the credit for innovations, but reality is seldom that simple. Here were two worlds coming together at both Derby and Longdon: the world of the iron masters, lively and experimental, and that of a new generation of canal engineers. It would have been surprising if they had not found similar answers to similar problems. We can never unravel the details today. However, we do have Telford writing in March 1795, describing the works of which he was taking charge, and mentioning the two Ellesmere aqueducts.[7]

> I have just recommended an Iron Aqueduct for the most considerable, it is approved, and will be executed under my direction, upon a principle entirely new, and which I am endeavouring to establish with regard to the application of Iron.

The Longdon aqueduct is a substantial affair. The original abutments were cut back and faced with stone on each side of the river, leaving a gap of 187 feet (57 metres) to be spanned by an iron trough, supported on three triangular iron piers set into masonry. The trough itself consists of twenty-six sections bolted together, with a towing path slung on the outside. The practical advantages of the system could hardly be seen to greater advantage than here, where the massive brick-and-masonry approach arches contrast with the light, almost delicate ironwork. Another advantage not so immediately obvious is that the iron aqueduct has to bear considerably less weight than the conventional. In order to keep a masonry aqueduct watertight, it has to be puddled, lined with heavy clay; the iron trough has no need of puddle. It is very clear that the iron trough can be carried on far less substantial supports than the masonry, and the implications of this for the crossing of the Dee valley must have been obvious to any competent engineer.

Now, we must float out on to the muddy waters of considering who should take credit for introducing the concept of the iron trough at Pontcysyllte. Telford had certainly been thinking about the use of iron for aqueducts in a general way, and with that great good fortune that seemed to follow him in his early career, he was unexpectedly thrust into a position where he was able to collaborate with one of the greatest iron makers of the age, a man who knew both how to make iron and how to use it. There can surely be no doubt that much of the detailed planning on how the sections should be cast and erected lay with the experienced Reynolds, but the decision to try the revolutionary new idea ultimately rested with the engineer in charge, Telford. He was by now thoroughly enthused with the notion of using cast iron.

The floods of 1795 that had swept away Clowes's work had also demolished the old bridge over the Severn at Buildwas, and as Telford still retained his post as county surveyor, he was called on to design a replacement. He was familiar with the earlier iron bridge, but had his own ideas on how improvements could be made. The Darby bridge has a notably high arch, and there was a strong tendency for the abutments to be forced inwards, compressing the arch. Telford realised that by using a flatter arch, there would be considerably less pressure exerted. Before the plans were authorised he must already have consulted the Coalbrookdale Company, who had cast the parts for the first bridge, for they were already committed to the scheme before it was given official approval in April.[8]

> The Magistrates at this Session agreed with the Coalbrookdale Company to erect a cast iron bridge, of one arch over the Severn at Buildwas, the span of which is to be 130 feet, the width of the passage way 18 feet, and to erect the same in nine months, for the sum of £3,700, being considerably lower than if the same had been erected of stone.

The report could also have mentioned that although the span of the

Buildwas bridge was 30 feet longer than that at Ironbridge, only half the weight of iron was used – 173 tons against 378 tons. Telford had grasped one important fact about the earlier bridge: that, much as he admired it, he felt that the builders had not 'disentangled their minds from the form of a stone arch'.[9] He realised that new materials demanded new methods.

> The span of the arch is 130 feet, and the rise is 24 feet; as the roadway could not with propriety be raised to a greater height, advantage was taken of the Schauffhausen principle by making the outer ribs rise to the top of the railing, and connecting them with the lower ribs by means of dove-tailed king-posts.[10]

Telford's bridge no longer exists, but it was a great success in its day. It did, however, prove rather more expensive than the original estimate of £3,700; the final amount calculated with that fine degree of accuracy which was a mark of accounting at the period came to: £6,034 13s. 3d.

It is quite extraordinary to think how far Telford had come in so short a time. Two years ago he had been a county surveyor, thinking in terms of a career as an architect. Now, here he was mastering a whole new set of technological skills, building canals and designing in iron as though he had been doing so all his working life. Meanwhile, Jessop was heavily engaged with other schemes, particularly the Grand Junction Canal, where he was busy preparing estimates, coping with severe problems at Blisworth tunnel and laying out the line of the Wendover Arm. It seems unlikely that the Ellesmere was at the forefront of his mind, whereas Telford must have been practically bursting with enthusiasm to try out his new-found skills on an even larger project. It was at this time that the idea first arose that an iron trough aqueduct offered the ideal solution for the crossing of the Dee. But, however great Telford's enthusiasm may have been, the decision was not his but Jessop's. It was Jessop who put the proposal to the committee in July 1795, by which time Telford had produced a revised line for the canal between Chester and Pontcysyllte.[11]

> It had been proposed to save expense in the Aqueduct at Pontcysylte to reduce the height 50 feet and descend and ascend by locks, but in due consideration I must now recommend to the Committee to make this saving by adopting an Iron Aqueduct at the full height originally intended which on correcting the Levels appears to be 125 feet above the surface of the water of the River Dee.
>
> The advantages that will attend the preservation of this level are too

obvious to need explanation. The arches or rather openings of the Aqueduct may be seven of 50 feet each the remainder may be raised by an
embankment, and this embankment will be formed by Earth to be boated
from the Cutting between the Dee and the Chirk valley – as few Hands can
be employed in this mode of working, and it will of course take much time
in the Execution, no time should be lost in beginning it.

This was, and is, the greatest achievement of the canal age. It was not
just the height and length of the aqueduct itself, but immense embankments had to be built to keep the canal at a level as it strode across the
valley, those at the southern end rising above a hundred feet. It all
needed to be planned with immense care, and Jessop was not surprisingly anxious.[12]

In looking forward to the time when we shall be laying the Iron Trough
on the Piers I foresee some difficulties that appear to be formidable – In
the first place I see the men giddy and terryfied in laying stones with such
an immense depth underneath them with only a space of 6 feet wide &
10 feet long to stand upon and the same want of room will hardly allow
space for the Beams and scaffolding while the Iron work is putting
together – I therefore think in the first, that in order to reduce the weight
of the Iron, or the parts of it – it will be better to have the openings narrow by adding another Pier, so as to have 8 openings of 52 feet from
Centre to Centre instead of 60 feet.
    In the next place I would have the Piers 7 feet wide at the Top instead
of 6 feet, and make them about 2 feet more in the other dimensions.

It was, in fact, to be August before the plans for the new aqueduct were
finally approved. Soon, Telford was at work on the embankments, but
the aqueduct itself was advanced only slowly.

It is easy to think of Telford at this time as a man wholly preoccupied
with his work, largely because so many of the surviving documents are
work related. But even among these, particularly in the letters
addressed to his old friend Matthew Davidson, there are many hints at
quite an active social life. At the end of 1796, he sent him a set of
'Geometrical Drawings' of Pontcysyllte, though there were still important decisions waiting to be taken, including the most important of all
– the number of piers to be built. This subject out of the way, he wanted to ask for help with a much more delicate matter – persuading the
church organist at Wrexham to tune 'Miss Alison's harp'. It was, as it
turned out, a wasted effort.[13]

I have received your Note and am now sorry that I gave you the trouble to go near that spiritual Doctor of Music – for I have this moment received a note from Mrs Alison, to say, they have at last recd a letter in which that Mr Randle has got such sublime notions and demands that it would require an Imperial Loan to satisfy him and that they are determined to go on without his assistance. I hope therefore that he has played you some very lofty Airs, for your trouble, and you have at any rate seen your favourite steeple.

Davidson himself was happy to be in Shropshire, enjoying life as a family man, and there is an easy friendliness about the Telford correspondence, even when the subject matter should have been treated with earnest solemnity – the war with France and the attempt to invade England through Ireland: 'The French have just been looking into Paddies Pantry, but they have met with a devil of a snifter from St. Patrick's wind hole. Have you another Tom yet? Live a thousand Years!!!'[14]

Just because we now have only occasional hints of a social life does not mean that he was any less gregarious than he had been in his days as county surveyor. He even managed a whole week's holiday with an unnamed companion to view the scenery of North Wales. The cult of the picturesque was at its height, and Telford succumbed. 'Cader Idris condescended to unfold his veil, just exhibited his rocky summit and instantly wrap himself up again in impenetrable Clouds'. He rhapsodised over what he saw: 'the immense Rocky Scenery – the mountain Torrents, Lakes and waterfalls, composed an awful, lonely magnificence'. But he still added that he came back via 'Davidson's famous Aqueduct, and which I can assure is already reckoned among the Wonders of Wales'.[15]

At the same time as work was languishing at Pontcysyllte, it was going forward on the second aqueduct at Chirk, which was also approached by a massive embankment. As with Pontcysyllte, the original plans called for a conventional aqueduct, and at first glance that is just what the aqueduct appears to be today. But look closer and one can see that the height of masonry above the ten spans is considerably less than in other aqueducts of the period. It does not contain puddled clay, the trough is actually lined with iron plates. The final agreed design was explained by Telford in a letter to Davidson:[16]

I have seen Mr. Jessop as to the Aqueduct at Chirk, and he agrees as to the general principle of the adopting Brick to Rubble Arches, instead of an Iron Trough, only that he thinks that the Piers should be set out so as to allow 6 feet instead of 5 feet on each side of the Canal – the distance

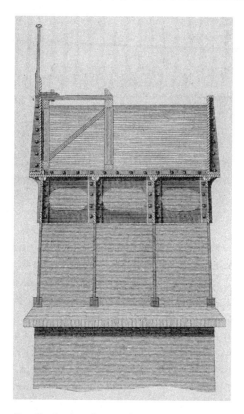

*Details showing the complex system of iron plates
used for the aqueduct trough at Pontcysyllte.*

between the Piers to be 45 feet, or if it would not increase the expense
very much, say 40 feet as John Simpson thinks that 45 is a great deal for
Brick Arches, but we should know the probable difference of expense
and Mr. Jessop wishes you to consider whether inverted Brick Arches laid
upon Flannel would not answer and be much cheaper than the stone
Bottom. But since I left Mr. Jessop I have been recollecting that in the
case of Brick Arches, that the Spandrels must be brought up Solid.

This change of Plan must not be divulged at present as the proposed
change must first be shewn to Mr. Myddleton.

Why was a simple iron trough not used, as at Pontcysyllte? Part of the
answer might be found in the last paragraph of the letter. Myddleton
was the owner of Chirk Castle, and although the Act of Parliament gave
the canal company considerable powers for purchasing land along the
route, the last thing they wanted was to get into conflict with powerful

landowners. Telford had noted elsewhere that Myddleton had 'universally shewn a disposition to render the Undertaking much service', but
it is possible that he indicated a preference for the classical elegance at
Chirk as an adjunct to his estate rather than the unashamed mod-
ernism of the iron trough. Not all landowners were so accommodating.
Some attempted to wring compensation out of the company for what
Telford called 'imaginary injuries to imaginary pleasure grounds'. One
local dignitary, a Dr. Harwood, demanded that the canal be kept out of
sight, but seemed to imagine that this could be achieved without any
disturbance to his peaceful life.[17]

> Dr Harwood has written me to day that the Navigators are making sad
> Havock in his ground. I should not wish that any unnecessary damage
> should be done, especially to the Dr, but I strongly suspect, that this must
> arise from the Line being thrown into deep Cutting, in order to accom-
> modate the Doctor, in which case, I think he should not be so forward
> and frequent in his complaints.

The complaints must have been particularly irritating at this time, when
Telford was at his busiest, though he made light of his cares at the end
of the letter: 'We had two very busy days at the Sessions and almost
wholly about Bridges. I think about a Dozen are ordered to be repaired.
To be sure this is nothing to a *Canal Man*.'

So it seems that Telford had already realised that this was indeed
where his future lay: not in architecture but in engineering.
Nevertheless, he did still have opportunities to practise his old skills. At
Grindley Brook, where the canal rises through a staircase of three
interconnected locks, he designed a charming little bow-fronted lock
cottage, its shape emphasised by a porch carried round it on wooden
pillars. The bay reappears in grander form at the canal company offices
at Ellesmere, in what is to all appearances a well-mannered Georgian
house. But it is the major engineering features that still demand attention, and which were still some way from completion as the eighteenth
century gave way to the nineteenth. Jessop, indeed, was so anxious to
complete the connection over the Dee, without which the canal was
deprived of its most valuable cargo, that he briefly contemplated the
notion of using the isolated piers that had already been constructed to
carry a railway, which would at that date have used horses for haulage,
instead of the canal. But soon the pace of work began to quicken, as the
national economy enjoyed a brief boom period from around 1799.

It was not only in the use of iron that the aqueducts showed innovative design features. At Chirk, the masonry was backed by brick, and the tops of the piers were left hollow, braced by cross walls on the in-terior. This represented a great saving in materials without any loss of strength. Similarly, the piers at Pontcysyllte were hollow above a height of 70 feet. The contract for supplying and erecting the ironwork went to William Hazeldine of the nearby Plas Kynaston ironworks – 'the arch conjuror Merlin Hazeldine', as Telford once called him. He and Telford were to enjoy a fruitful professional relationship spreading over many years. Telford left an account of the construction of Pontcysyllte.[18]

> The stone piers are 18 in number, beside the two abutment piers; they were all built to the level of 20 feet, and then the scaffolding and gang-ways were all raised to that level, and the materials being brought from the north bank; the workmen always commenced at the most distant or south abutment pier, receding pier by pier to the north bank; and by this ascending from time to time in their work, they felt no more apprehension of danger when on the highest, than at first on the lowest gangways.

He was proud of his safety record, though not notably charitable to the solitary victim; 'one man only fell during the whole of the operations in building the piers, and affixing the iron work upon their summit, and this took place from carelessness on his part'.[19] The aqueducts represented everything that was new in the technology of the age, though there is something rather homely about the material used for sealing the joints between the iron plates – Welsh flannel soaked in white lead. The only improvement offered a quarter of a century later was to replace the white lead with tar.[20]

In between the two aqueducts, the rising ground was pierced by a quarter-mile-long tunnel (420 metres) which began near the end of Chirk aqueduct and emerged into a deep cutting at the far side. The tunnel was also unusual for its time in that it was built to a sufficient width to take a towpath. On most canals at that time, horses had to be led over the top of a tunnel while the boatmen slowly pushed their boat through by walking their feet along the tunnel walls – legging the boat. It represented greater expense to the company but greatly speeded traffic on the canal. The final run to Ruabon was completed on a railway. In 1804, authorisation was given for a narrow, but navigable waterway to be cut from close to the northern end of Pontcysyllte, along the valley of the Dee past Llangollen, to a point where it reached the river itself. Here, a large weir was constructed, and river water fed in to supply the canal. It is ironic that the canal should now be universally known by the name of this afterthought which winds and wiggles its way to Llangollen.

The great event in the history of the whole enterprise was the opening of Pontcysyllte on 26 November 1805, which received national attention.[21] The Shropshire Volunteers turned out with two field pieces for firing salutes and played patriotic airs. Banners were carried with messages ranging from the poetic:

> Here conquer'd Nature owns Britannia's sway
> While Oceans' realms her matchless deeds display

to the mundane, but apposite: 'Success to the iron trade of Great Britain, of which Pontcysyllte aqueduct is a specimen'. The 'barges' crossed the aqueduct, there were speeches, and then they all came back again.

> The discharge from the guns, as the procession returned, the plaudits of the spectators (calculated at full 8,000), the martial music, the echo reverberating from the mountains, magnified the enchanting scene; and the countenance of every one present bespoke the satisfaction with which they contemplated this very useful and stupendous work.

The printed card handed round to the spectators listed those responsible, naming Telford as 'The Engineer', John Simpson, the contractor, Hazeldine for the ironwork, Davidson as superintendent and William Davies as having the contract for the earthworks. Telford was widely praised in the speechmaking, and the ovation by Rowland Hunt spoke of 'our General Agent, Mr Telford; who, with the advice and judgement of our eminent and much respected Engineer, Mr Jessop, invented, and with unabated diligence carried the whole into execution'. This was virtually the only reference to Jessop, and Charles Hadfield has argued at great length that this was part of an intentional scheme by Telford to claim more credit than he was entitled to and, at the same time, to remove all credit from the company's senior engineer.[22]

It is certainly true that at the very end of his life, when he was preparing his autobiography, he played down Jessop's role or, at any rate, chose not to mention it, concentrating on his own part in the proceedings. He would seem to have had a problem in deciding how to write of his relationship with Jessop and the start of the Ellesmere construction, for in his first draft this section has been repeatedly crossed out and amended. An elderly and distinguished man at the very end of his career can be forgiven for blowing his own trumpet. This is very different from a young man deliberately falsifying the record at the expense of his superior. And this is the serious charge laid against Telford which, if found to be proven, casts a very dark shadow over his character. So it cannot be ignored.

That Telford was ambitious is not to be denied. That he was prepared to make use of influential friends is clear. Nothing else in the record, however, shows him to be guilty of duplicity. It seems unlikely that the full facts will ever be known. Hadfield makes a number of assumptions, in particular that all the material printed at the time was produced specifically to Telford's orders – an assumption for which there is no evidence whatsoever. But if it was not done with Telford's connivance, why should Jessop's name be so insignificant in comparison with his? Various possibilities suggest themselves. One is that those concerned recognised, as Hunt's oration stated – and he, as a long-term committee member and former chairman, was ideally placed to know all the facts – that the inspiration was indeed Telford's. William Jessop was a famously modest man, not much interested in official celebrations; he did not even put in an appearance at the opening. It was simply not his style. Jessop was sixty years old. He was happily married with a family of eight children. He had more than enough work in hand and a reputation that was second to none. He neither needed, nor particularly welcomed, any more public acclaim. Is it not also possible that it was this generous man who suggested that, as the plan had first been formulated by his younger colleague, who was still at the beginning of his career, the plaudits should be received by him? This would be wholly in character for Jessop – just as it would not be out of character for Telford to accept any help freely offered. Unlike Jessop, he had no family or other ties; his work was at the very core of his life. Two sets of circumstances tend to support this view. Firstly, Jessop was still chief engineer: had he wished to set the record straight, he could have overruled Telford with ease. Secondly, he continued to work amicably with Telford. If he nursed a grievance, it never showed, and Telford never spoke of the older man other than in terms of admiration.

We cannot reconstruct all the events of 1805, but at the very least it has to be said that the case against Telford is not proven. Charles Hadfield and the author argued over this one for years, neither ever finally convincing the other. Readers should perhaps look at the more detailed arguments spelled out in Hadfield's book, and then make up their own minds. Whatever the politics surrounding the building of Pontcysyllte, nothing can diminish the grandeur of the structure itself: 1007 feet (307 metres) long and 127 (39 metres) at its highest above the Dee, it remains a spectacular tribute to the imagination and skill of all who were involved in its construction.

CHAPTER FIVE

A Busy and Varied Life

Long before the opening of Pontcysyllte, Telford was heavily engaged in a number of other projects, not all of which were to come to fruition. In our own age of ever-increasing specialisation, it is astonishing to contemplate the range of his activities. To his other skills he now added authorship, not the amateur poems with which he once diverted himself, but serious technical papers. Having worked as an engineer on two canals in the Shropshire area, he was an obvious choice as author for Joseph Plymley's reference book on Shropshire. It is more puzzling to work out why he should have been chosen to write a treatise on mills for the Board of Agriculture, a subject of which, as far as we know, he had no practical experience. But he wrote just such a treatise in 1798, and a most curious document it proves to be. The actual discussion of mill mechanisms contains nothing new; much of it is a rehash of Smeaton's earlier experiments on mill efficiency, to which Telford added a certain amount of information on horizontal mills gleaned from Jessop. His own contribution is an ambitious scheme which linked providing water for navigation with operating a succession of mills. He called for a series of reservoirs to be built near the headwaters of major rivers and joined together by navigable canals. The canals would also act as land drains. At times of drought, water could be fed into the river, and at other times, the excess water could be used to turn the mills. All water would eventually be returned to the rivers. It sounds like the best of all possible worlds, but like all such schemes which too closely resemble perpetual-motion machines, there is a flaw. You cannot successfully impound water in the catchment area without reducing the natural flow in the river, and keeping this delicate system in balance would have been an all but impossible task. What he was proposing was, in effect, something not dissimilar to a modern hydroelectric scheme, with the turbine of the power station the equivalent to Telford's water mills, and as we now know, such schemes do not come into being without a price. Perhaps the best that can be said for the treatise on mills is that it is very attractively illustrated.

There may have been a second agenda at work here, however. Telford had already made the acquaintance of Sir John Sinclair, who had been actively involved in promoting canal bills. It may well be that the request to write for the Board came initially through him – and it was certainly Sinclair who wrote offering official government thanks for his efforts.[1]

> The Zeal you have displayed for promoting the Objects of the Board of Agriculture, merits not only the thanks of the Board and of the Public, but also that you should have it in your power to wear some Public Mark of our approbation – I request therefore your Acceptance of the Set of Buttons herewith sent.

Telford had long since learned that work done well for men of influence was worth a great deal more than the money received in fees. The Sinclair connection was to do no harm at all to his future career.

As a new convert to the world of engineering, Telford bubbled with enthusiasm. His Shropshire churches were good enough in their way, but he must have seen that they were minor additions to a country with an immense heritage of ecclesiastical architecture, stretching right back to the Anglo-Saxons and Celts. On the Ellesmere Canal, he was blasting away the side of a mountain to create a waterway and thrusting canals high above river valleys to the amazement of thousands. There was no competition: better a great engineer than a second-rate architect. His head buzzed with ideas, his notebooks and letters were full of plans and schemes, and all the time he was learning, teaching himself everything from philosophy and economics to chemistry and mechanics. And it seemed the whole world was open to him, there was nothing he could not do – or if he could not do something already he was confident that he could soon teach himself. Everything he wrote to his friends was full of optimism for the future, though not everything proved the success he had hoped. There was, however, still traditional work to be put in hand, and even here he showed a new confidence.

His Shropshire connections remained intact, and he was to retain a close interest in the Severn and its bridges. In 1798, he designed a new bridge at Bewdley. In spite of his enthusiasm for iron, this is a wholly conventional masonry design, and one of his most elegant. The river is crossed on three arches, with pilasters rising above the cut waters to an intricate parapet topped by a splendid stone balustrade. The work went on at a tremendous rate, with stone brought down-river from nearby Arley, and Telford added yet another reliable man to his growing entourage of trusted collaborators and employees. The ability to find and keep good men played a large part in Telford's success and he knew it. He was not, at least in this instance, at all unwilling to share the praise for what he clearly saw as a prestigious undertaking.[2]

> We have had a remarkably dry Summer and Autumn. The dry season has been against the working upon Canals, but it has enabled us to raise Bewdley Bridge, as by enchantment we have thus raised a magnificent Bridge over the River Severn in one Season, which is not contemptible work, for John Simpson and your humble Servant, amidst so many other and still great Undertakings. But John Simpson is a treasure of talents and integrity – I met with him here by chance, employed and recommended him, and he has now all the works of any magnitude in this great and rich district.

Telford was soon to be involved in improving the navigation of the river above Bewdley, as far as Ironbridge. Those who know the river today might be amazed at the idea of anything larger than a rowing boat navigating the upper reaches of the Severn, but in Telford's time it was common for quite large vessels, including trows, the traditional sailing barges of the river, to be found loading with cargo at the Coalbrookdale wharf.

He had now found himself accepted as something of an expert in the field of canals, and like most experienced engineers of the day he discovered there was a good deal of profitable work in surveying and commenting on the works and plans of colleagues, and providing evidence for and against the various schemes as they came up for consideration by Parliament. He was not overenamoured of being entangled – 'lawyer like' as he put it – in this side of the business, but, as he ruefully admitted, it was 'the way of the world'. And if it did nothing else, this entanglement with other engineers and promoters was constantly acquiring for him new contacts, and ultimately new contracts. On a trip to the west coast in 1799, he was able to make a shrewd assessment of future trends and developments.[3]

Bristol is sinking in its commercial importance, it is not well situated, and its Merchants are rich and indolent. It will dwindle away. Liverpool is young, vigorous and well situated, it has besides taken Root in the country by means of the Canals – another port will arise somewhere in the Severn, but Liverpool will become of the first commercial importance.

He did find time, however, to call in at the church of St Mary Redcliffe in Bristol to 'worship at the Shrine of Chatterton'. He still retained his passion for poetry. More importantly, on his return from the trip he also called in at the Soho Works, Birmingham, where Boulton and Watt were busily manufacturing steam engines, for which at the time they had a near monopoly. He met James Watt, a fellow Scot, and his son, and declared Watt to be 'great and good'. Another close friendship was forged, and a new commercial attachment established. Seeds were sown on this trip that were soon to come to fruition, for it was not long before Telford was back on the west coast and plans were pushed a little further along.[4]

You know I am toss'd about like a Tennis Ball, the other day I was in London, since that I have been in Liverpool, and in a few days I expect to be in Bristol. – such is my fortune – and to tell you a bit of a secret, I truly believe, that it suits my disposition, I am at present engaged in conducting a Plan for supplying the town of Liverpool with water by means of pipes, in the same manner as London is now supplied, this is a business of some magnitude, and we have some opposition to contend with – no less than the *Corporation of Liverpool* – thus circumstanced, you will readily conceive, that my mind must be occupied in forming proper arrangements.

It was just as well that Telford developed a strong taste for travelling and bustling between various engineering schemes, for this was to be the pattern for the rest of his days. The Liverpool Water Works was not a very large concern by the standards of the time, slightly smaller than the modest Lambeth Waterworks, begun in 1785, and to which Telford was presumably referring. Water was to be pumped up by steam engine, the first of many that he was to order from Boulton and Watt. It was a simple beam engine with an 18-inch-diameter cylinder, which is really quite small by the standards of the day, working 12-inch pumps. Readers who know the Boulton and Watt engine of a slightly later date at Crofton on the Kennet and Avon Canal can make a direct comparison, for that 1812 engine has a 42-inch cylinder, driving a 30-inch pump.

That might give some idea of the scale of the operations. Gibb notes that 'there was said to be' a supply rate of 120,000 gallons an hour at Liverpool, but that sounds very optimistic. Telford was to be involved with public waterworks again, and he was certainly to make increasing use of steam power over the years. The business might also have aroused his interest in the subject of pipe work, as he found himself collaborating with a Shropshire man John Howell who had invented a machine for boring wooden pipes. Howell lacked the capital to develop his invention, so Telford took out a patent on his behalf. It must have seemed an astute investment, for it was 'a beautifully simple machine' which he was able to use at Liverpool. He was to discover, however, as many others had done, that holding a patent and enforcing it are not at all the same thing. And, as he might have foreseen, the age of the wooden pipe was coming to an end as cast iron became more common.

It sometimes seems at this stage that Telford was a bit like a deprived small boy who had just been given the key to a wonderful toy cupboard. He wanted to try everything and was sure everyone would share his enthusiasm.[5]

> Some fresh Game has been started lately, of still a finer breed – but when the chase will end is at present problematical – I therefore mention it to you in confidence – there is a board of five members appointed to act as a Board of Control over all the Inland Navigations &c of Ireland – one of the Members is a particular friend of mine, and is at this moment a pupil, as it were, anxious for information on the subject. This is a Noble object, the field is wide, and new ground, capable of improvement beyond even the reach of common apprehensions – To take up and manage the Water of a fine Island – is likely a fairy tale – and if properly conducted may prove the means of rendering it a Jewell among the Nations.

It was to remain a dream.

His enthusiasm for inventions and inventors was aroused by news of a young man, James Douglas, who came from Bigholms, a hamlet just three miles or so away from Telford's own native Langholm. This was itself a recommendation and Telford promptly christened him the 'Eskdale Archimedes'. He had apparently been living in America, where he had acquired a sound reputation as a mechanical engineer, and had returned to Britain with a recommendation to the Society of Arts. Telford was keen to meet him, and once they had made contact he was well satisfied with the inventor, who seemed prepared to turn his hand and brain to a bewildering variety of problems. This fitted in well with Telford's own mood at the time.[6]

> I have just had a letter from Douglas – he has got his patent secured for
> the Brick Machine, and the Patent for the Shearing Machine is in great
> forwardness – He informs me that he has invented a Ball for destroying
> the Rigging of Ships the plan of which Admiral Pasley has laid before
> Lord Spencer – tho he is not sanguine of much success on acct of the
> expense – Douglas is a very ingenious man and might do much service
> to the nation, were it not that honest John Bull with his national blunt-
> ness likes to trudge on in the trammels of system.

Telford was now to recruit him to the ranks of his trusted aides as he
embarked on by far his most ambitious project to date, not out in the
hills of Wales nor even in the growing port of Liverpool, but in the very
heart of the capital.

London's prosperity was then centred on the River Thames, with
its busy traffic of coastal vessels and larger ships trading to Europe,
America and Asia. By the middle of the eighteenth century, it was
estimated that over 8000 vessels a year were entering the river, making
it Britain's busiest port. The scene must have been one of immense
confusion, for there were no enclosed docks along the river, and the
ships rode at their moorings on the tidal water, loaded and unloaded
by fleets of lighters. London was falling behind other ports such as
Liverpool, Hull and even sluggish Bristol, where new docks were
being developed. It was clear that something had to be done to
improve a system in which overcrowding was not the only problem.
The open quays and wharves had turned pilfering into a major
industry, and one commentator of the day, Patrick Colquhon,
estimated that by the end of the century, at least 10,000 thieves
depended on the river for a full-time living. As a result, a very powerful
committee of West Indies merchants threatened to leave the Thames
for good. Something had to be done, and a very businesslike report
was produced, proposing a whole range of improvements based on
the construction of new docks.[7] Consequently, the attention of the
leading engineers of the day was concentrated on London, William
Jessop and John Rennie among them. Telford was as interested as
any, and sent a long letter to Little[8] setting out what proposals were
being put forward, and hinting that he, too, might find a role in
these new, exciting developments. He must have realised that he was
far too inexperienced to play a major part in the dock scheme, so
he concentrated his attention instead on another problem besetting
London's river.

All shipping on its way upstream from the sea was brought to an abrupt halt at London's one and only bridge, in place since medieval times. Houses had been built on top, so that a commentator writing in the sixteenth century described it as 'rather a continuall streete than a bridge'. Over the years, the houses had been removed and the street broadened, which was fine as far as the traffic over the bridge was concerned, but was no help at all to boatmen passing underneath. The bridge was built over nineteen narrow arches, through which the constricted water rushed at high speed, so that taking a small boat through was a decidedly hazardous business, a bit like shooting the rapids. It placed severe restrictions on the size of vessels able to pass upstream, and there were already alarming signs that the venerable structure was not in the best condition – London Bridge was indeed falling down.

For a time, Telford kept the details of what he was planning from even his closest friends, but it eventually emerged that he had been collaborating with Douglas on plans for a new London Bridge, built not of stone, but of iron. Details were duly presented to the London Port Parliamentary Committee, headed by such grandees as William Pitt and Sir Joseph Banks. It was a bold venture, and might have been dismissed out of hand if the evidence of Telford's Buildwas bridge had been all they had to go on. It has to be remembered that Buildwas was only the second iron bridge, and although in many ways it was an improvement on the first, it was not wholly successful. It used two different types of rib in construction, which reacted differently both to changing loads and to changes in the temperature, the latter effect, in particular, resulting in severe cracking. It had to be patched with fish plates – not perhaps the most elegant of solutions, but the bridge held up perfectly well until 1906.

A far more successful bridge was thrown over the River Wear at Sunderland in 1796, built by Walkers of Rotherham to a patented design by the local MP, Rowland Burden. Built of six segmental ribs in cast iron, with wrought-iron straps, it was a majestic span of 236 feet (72 metres). It has an interesting history in that an earlier proposal for an iron bridge had been made by the revolutionary writer Tom Paine, a great author but a wretched engineer. It has been suggested that the Sunderland bridge was based on Paine's design and that castings for a bridge proposed by him were used. This was not so. The Sunderland bridge represented a major advance in construction using iron, as important in its way as the first canal aqueducts, and it certainly had a profound effect on Telford's thinking. So it was that, in July 1800, when the parliamentary committee went to investigate the site of the proposed new London bridge, they carried plans for a cast-iron bridge 'on the improved plan of the Sunderland Bridge'. Telford was cautiously optimistic.[9]

> Whether this great undertaking is carried into execution to the extent of the Plans or any extent, it is certainly true that the Report of the select Committee and the Plans and Propositions they have approved and recommended, are founded entirely upon and are little else than an abstract of the plans, Estimates and explanations and informations afforded them by Mr. Douglas and myself. So far the triumph is certainly complete. Many points remain yet to be adjusted before it can be said that the business is in a proper train. I hope and trust it will be managed by a Parliamentary Commission, and if so it is not unlikely that a considerable portion of the weight may come to rest upon the shoulders of your humble Serv[t]. at least I can perceive that at present this is the quarter that is looked to for real business; and if they will provide the ways and means and give me Elbow Room – I see my way as plainly as mending the Brig at the Harbour.

By then, the committee had approved the idea of an iron bridge, and Telford and Douglas had been hard at work modifying their designs. It was an astonishing affair, a graceful arch of iron, carried across the river in a single giant leap of 600 feet. In drawings, it looked so delicate that a gust might blow it away, but scale was deceptive. Telford had calculated that 6500 tons of cast iron would need to be used. Bearing in mind the problems he had encountered at Buildwas with a mere 173 tons, this was not merely a giant leap across space but an even greater one of daring imagination. He realised it would need massive abutments and budgeted for over 12,000 cubic metres of granite blocks and 520 cubic metres of brickwork. Not surprisingly, the committee set about finding experts to comment on this astonishing structure, while Telford began a promotional campaign on behalf of his design.

He turned to his old friend, the iron master William Reynolds, who was very supportive.[10]

> My Dear Friend
> In reply to yours of the 8th Inst on mature consideration I think your plan for the Iron Bridge excellent & do not foresee the least difficulty in its execution for tho I do not from your letter or sketch at all comprehend what size or weight your scantlings of Iron will be, yet I imagine be they what they may as they will all be cast out of a reverbatory furnace the Pig Iron may be so selected that very little variation in the contraction of the pieces will take place a mill may be contrived to adjust them by grinding.

The only problem that he could see was of a heavy, swaying waggon setting up sympathetic vibrations with the bridge – 'I shd literally tremble to stand on the centre thereof'.

When, however, the committee applied to James Walker, the only man who had any experience of a construction coming anywhere near this scale, while he did not condemn the design, he certainly did not approve it. He declined to answer a series of questions sent by the committee on the grounds that answering them would involve 'much investigation, much experiment as well as local knowledge'. He did, however, sound a note of scepticism, pointing out that the Sunderland span had been measured as rising 37 inches at the crown on a hot summer's day. He left the committee to draw their own conclusions about what might happen with a span well over double that length. His final summary was not exactly encouraging.[11]

> Your idea of an Arch of 600 feet is a bold stretch – Tom Paine's opinion was, that a Bridge upon his System might be thrown over the Atlantic if Centers for creating it could have been fixed. We have however Liv'd to see his System of Bridges, as well as of Politics, exploded.

Telford, however, was pushing ahead with detailed plans, and at this stage the darkest cloud on the horizon seemed to be blowing from Europe.[12]

> The French are like Paddy's Racer – Driving all before them – The Austrians seem beaten at all points, and certainly must conclude a separate peace. How far we shall partake of the blessings and woes of the impending negotiations is beyond the Reach of my telescope – I am afraid they do not argue favourably to my projects, and to tell you the truth I shall not be surprised if the whole scheme is abandoned until some accident happens at London Bridge.

In the meantime, he was arranging for various tests on material strengths to be made, and receiving encouraging support from his old friends, especially from those who knew nothing about engineering – 'there will be nothing like in the whole Solar System except the rings of Saturn'.[13] Telford even went so far as to start contemplating the embellishments he might make.[14]

> I would make the outside Rib in the Gothic manner on account of the lightness and elegance of the forms, their being well adapted for the ornamenting Iron work and admit of finishing the top and Railing with Gothic work & Pinnacles for securing the Lamps.

He was encouraged to commission an illustration of the bridge to get public opinion on his side, and it was duly published. No one can be other than impressed by the beautiful simplicity and boldness of the design. It looks absolutely magnificent and, if built, would have been one of the great bridges of the world – assuming that it could have been built at all. There must have been grave doubts as to whether even the massive abutments he proposed could have supported such a work. As it was, the scheme was never to reach fruition.

The failure of the plan was a great disappointment to Telford, even though he had forecast it, as was the sudden, totally unexplained, departure of James Douglas, who Telford remarked had 'played us a Plishey'. It was inconvenient both to Telford and to John Pasley, the same Pasley who had first helped him to find work in London and was now backing the scheme. It still rankled years later.[15]

> At Inverness I was surprised by a letter from James Douglass announcing his successful career in France. – I am not surprised at it, he was peculiarly fitted for that country. I have never heard of him since he left Mr. Pasley and myself in the lurch, which action, with good reason, soured the mind of that most excellent of men, even to me (whom the good old man had forced into the connection) he became estranged altho' comparatively my injury was greater than his. – but of this no more, I wish Douglas may deserve his success, which his natural talents merit, altho' they might have been exercised in a more respectable manner, but he was impatient for distinction and Wealth, for which in this country he found too many able Competitors.

Telford, it seems, had conveniently forgotten his own glowing opinions of the young man at the time. In the event, the huge effort expended on this abortive scheme was not entirely wasted. It brought Telford's name to the attention of yet more men of influence, singled him out as a man of bold imagination, while at the same time the failure of the project could clearly be seen as in no way the fault of the engineer, but entirely due to a change in the political and economic climate. He should perhaps have thanked the politicians for keeping his reputation intact.

In the midst of all this frantic activity, he still showed that his passion for poetry was undimmed, and found his very own protégé in the young Scots poet, Thomas Campbell. He and the Rev. Archibald Alison decided to take Campbell under their wings, and exchanged views on his work, each it seems as extravagant in his praise as the other. In an undated letter of 1802, Telford wrote:

There has never been any thing like him – he is the very spirit of Parnassus. Have you seen his 'Lochiel'? He will surpass everything, ancient or modern – your Pindars, your Drydens, and your Grays. I expect nothing short of a Scotch Milton, a Shakespeare, or something more than either! I hope he will take up a subject which will oblige him to collect all his powers, and exert them in a manner that will Stamp their value to the latest posterity.

Telford had by now established himself in rooms in London, very appropriately at the Salopian Coffee House. Campbell enthusiastically took up an invitation to stay, enjoying the engineer's affable character and certainly valuing the introductions to London social life. Telford's motive, however, was rather different. He wanted to keep him 'in check' and keep his mind on his writing. His poem 'Gertrude' was received with extravagant praise in Scotland. Alison described how a friend had gone away to read it in private and returned 'pale as a ghost and literally sick with weeping'. Telford was clearly not convinced that such adulation was good for the young man.[16]

Unusually frequent visits plainly bespoke the parental anxiety respecting the reception of 'Gertrude' in his native city – and from 'the friends of his heart'. I almost blame myself for this rashness. Such unqualified applause will either drive him frantic, or make him complete the epic poem on 'Bruce', which he has threatened, before he closes his eyes.

Between them, Alison and Telford managed to get Campbell fixed up with a small stipend in Sydenham, but, alas, the great work never materialised and his name has long since slipped into obscurity. It says a good deal for Telford's generosity of spirit that at this busy and crucial stage of his career he could still make time to encourage and help a young poet. The demands on his time, however, were about to increase in a dramatic fashion.

CHAPTER SIX

Back to the Highlands

Of all the influential men who helped Telford further his career, there was perhaps none more important than Sir John Sinclair. We have already met him in his official capacity, congratulating the engineer on his publications, but he was also in a position to offer Telford work of the greatest importance. Sinclair came from an ancient Scottish family, former earls of Caithness and Orkney. As soon as he inherited his father's Caithness estate at the very young age of sixteen, he set about improving it, building a road over a previously all but impassable mountain. He quickly became involved with a committee of the Highland Society, investigating ways of improving the breeds of local sheep. The Society, however, was to develop far broader aims: nothing less than the general improvement of the economy of the region and the life of the people. Sinclair's interest, however, stretched beyond the local scene, and he moved on to Westminster, where he became an enthusiastic advocate of the establishment of a Board of Agriculture. Once it was set up, Sinclair was an almost automatic choice as first president. So, here we have a man at the very heart of public affairs and government, who was also a passionate advocate of improvements to his native Highlands. He also saw that the best way forward, perhaps the only way forward, was through public works. In modern parlance, nothing could be done until a sound infrastructure was in place, and for that he needed the services of a good engineer. It was only natural that he should turn to the man who had not only dazzled London with a scheme of sparkling originality, but was also a good, sound, patriotic Scot.

One of Sinclair's interests lay with what was then the small settlement of Wick in the far north-east of Scotland, where as well as trying to set up small industries he was also developing the harbour for herring boats. The matter was taken up with the British Fisheries Society, who were actually – though not very actively – engaged in improving facilities for fishing fleets. Telford was, it seems, at first reporting solely to Sinclair, who had personally commissioned the Wick improvements, but it brought him into the British Fisheries circle. It was not long before he was being officially described as their principal engineer. This was not a very demanding task, as the Society had little in the way of funds to allocate. For Telford, it was one job among many, and almost certainly not the most important in his eyes. Yet it was this connection that was to provide him with work for almost all the rest of his professional life. He was also to have the immense satisfaction of knowing that he had made a huge contribution not just to his native land of Scotland, but he had also helped materially to change the lives of the poorest and most oppressed of its citizens.

As a Lowland Scot, Telford had not experienced the miseries of the Highlanders, who had been unfortunate enough to back the wrong – that is, losing – side in 1745. Many English still regarded the Scots as an alien, barbaric race. Even James Boswell, himself a Scot, commented to Dr Johnson that being surrounded by the locals at Auchnasheal was 'much the same as being with a tribe of Indians'. To which Johnson laconically replied: 'Yes, sir: but not so terrifying.'[1] Other English visitors were even less charitable. One had scarcely crossed the border before he let rip.[2]

> My eyes encountered, in a cluster of mud-built sheds, a number of miserable wretches, ragged, bare-footed and squalid, almost beyond the power of description. Nor was this misery confined to a single spot: for it attended every village, and almost every countenance I met with, in my way to Glasgow. Such wretchedness is naturally the offspring of idleness, ignorance and necessity … this deplorable state of the common people greatly discredits a country to which nature has been in other respects very munificent.

And this was written half a century after the rebellion of 1745. It was, of course, convenient to represent the miseries of the Scots as being entirely their own fault, totally unconnected with policies decided in Westminster. Parliament was determined to break up the old feudal system of the clans, no bad thing in itself, but they achieved this often with a vicious cruelty and with no thought of what was to go in its place. The former chieftains lost not just their power, but also the sense of responsibility that had kept the system intact for centuries. A new generation of landowners, caring little or nothing for tradition, looked to profit first and left tradition to tag along behind where it would. Crofters were evicted to make way for sheep runs, in the long, agonising process that became known as 'The Highland Clearances'. The Highlanders, forbidden to wear the plaid, discouraged from speaking Gaelic and liable to be dispossessed of everything they had at the whim of a landowner, were inevitably almost totally demoralised. They had neither the will nor the means to raise themselves out of degrading poverty in their own land, and many abandoned the attempt and set off overseas to try for a new life. There was a general recognition developing that something was seriously wrong, and if that wrong was not righted there could be troubled times ahead. Telford was one of those who saw the dangers all too clearly.[3]

> I wish the Clans do not burst out with open rebellion – I mean with each other – *they are mad bodies*. but matters are changed, the chieftains may fight each other, the *de'el in highland man* will stir for them – the Lairds have transferred their affections from the people to the flocks of sheep – and the people have lost their veneration for the Lairds – it is the natural progress of Society, but it is not a pleasant change. There was great happiness in the patriarchal state of Clanship – they are now hastening into the opposite extreme. It is wrong.

By the end of the eighteenth century, it was clear even in London that simply to deplore 'idleness and ignorance' was as irrational as it was unhelpful. If improvement was to come then it needed to be given a chance. One of Scotland's besetting problems was a lack of good roads and communications. There had been a spurt of road building by the military, following the two rebellions of 1715 and 1745, creating a network wholly designed to link forts to control the population. Generally known as 'Wade's roads', after the general who began the system, they were not generally very well or very sensibly constructed. The military engineers seemed determined to keep to the valleys for as long as they could, and then when it became impossible to stay at a low level they climbed out over high passes, often through a series of elaborate zig-zags. Today it is almost impossible to believe that the footpath that climbs north out of Glencoe, known as The Devil's Staircase, was once a military road that was intended for use by wheeled vehicles. It is quite bad enough puffing up the path with a full rucksack.

Here was a country beginning to suffer from severe depopulation, where the dispossessed could only be persuaded to stay if new employment could be found. The growth of a fishing industry around the coast seemed to offer a viable alternative to agricultural work for many, but any scheme that could be devised would depend on a decent system of communication. Building roads, harbours and canals seemed a splendid option. It would not only provide a basis for future development over the long term, but it would provide direct employment in the short term. On top of which a whole generation would learn new skills and, just as importantly, rediscover the will to work. In 1801, the government decided to act, and they turned to Thomas Telford.

In July 1801, Telford received a note asking him to investigate ways of improving the fishing industry in Scotland.[4] It was from Nicholas Vansittart, Joint Secretary to the Treasury, one of the group who had been looking at the London Bridge proposals. He was asked to get straight on with the job, 'as you are perfectly acquainted with the objects proposed by the Fishery Society and have a general knowledge of the intentions of Government'. Detailed instructions were to follow later, but Whitehall was not capable of working with the speed of Thomas Telford when his enthusiasm was in full flow. By the time he was told what to do, he had all but done it. When the instructions reached him in September, however, they contained a new element which had nothing to do with the interests of the Fisheries Society.

> In that part of your Survey which now remains they have another object of great importance in view. Namely the making the Harbours on the North Eastern Coast subservient to the purposes of commerce with the Northern parts of Europe, and occasionally useful to His Majesty's Navy. These purposes appear likely to be best answered by the Murray Firth or the Firth of Cromarty, and they therefore wish you to examine both these inlets with particular attention, obtaining from the neighbouring inhabitants as much information as possible respecting the Tides, Currents, Depth of Water and other circumstances affecting the Navigation. You will also examine the most convenient situation for the Erection of Towns or Villages, and for building and repairing Ships, as far as your Judgment goes, consider how far any of these Harbours are capable of defence against an Enemy.

This was just the sort of work to appeal to Telford: travelling widely through his beloved Scotland and engaging in a project which promised real and tangible benefits to his fellow countrymen. His mood bubbles from the page in this letter written from Peterhead.[5]

> Having completed all that was necessary to be done on the Spot, as to
> my Western and Northern Surveys, I am arrived at this Eastern extrem-
> ity of our Rocky Isle and which is very properly composed of Granite ...
> I do believe there never was a season more favourable for a business of
> this kind ... I have caried regular Surveys along the Rainy West,
> through the middle of the tempestuous wilds of Lochaber, on each side
> of the far famed Johnny Groats, around the shores of Cromarty,
> Inverness and Fort George and likewise the Coast of Murrray, and all
> this without being interrupted *one day*. The apprehension of the
> weather changing for the worse, has prompted me to incessant and
> hard labour, so that I am now almost lame and blind; I have, however,
> I trust now nearly accomplished all the main objects of my mission –
> and shall be able to make out a plan and surveys of one of the noblest
> projects that was ever laid before a Nation.

He noted that although agriculture was generally in a good state, the
development of a fishing industry was severely hampered by the lack of
good harbours. He also noted that one of the great problems in northern Scotland was a lack of good fuel. Awareness of potential problems
did nothing to dampen his good spirits and the letter ends in jocular
good humour.

> From hence I shal proceed along the coast, to the Firth of Forth, if I am
> not swallowed up in the *Bullers of Buchan*, which will be very provoking,
> after having encountered the Ord of Caithness and the Suters of
> Cromarty.

Careering headlong around the Scottish coast, he could not even
find time to take a few days off to travel inland for a visit to Eskdale,
and even the letter he sent to the Littles was brief. Telford then
reported at length to Vansittart, giving detailed notes on what he had
seen and what he proposed.[6] He suggested developing major harbour
facilities at Oban and Peterhead, which could be of use to the Navy,
and building new harbours at Wick and Thurso for the fishing fleets.
These schemes, however, were of less importance than the main
proposal that would form the heart of all new development.

> I consider the leading features of the Plan by which these great objects
> may be accomplished to consist of the forming a complete Inland Naviga-
> tion (fit to receive vessels of all Burthens) from Loch Beauley to Loch Eil,
> and adjacent to each extremity of this Navigation, to provide a Harbour fit
> to receive, supply and refit and repair not only the vessels employed in the
> Fishing, and general commerce, but likewise Ships of war.

By the Surveys I have made, I am convinced that a navigation may be formed from Inverness to Fort William of the description which is wanted. The line is very direct, and I have observed no serious obstacle in any part of it. The rise between the shores is trifling, and on the summit there is an inexhaustible supply of water. The Entrances from the Navigation into the Sea, are immediately in deep water, good anchoring ground, and in places of perfect safety at Inverness and Fort William – From these two points, and before the vessels can reach the open Sea, there are excellent Harbours, say Oban and Tobermory on the West and Cromarty on the east side of the Island.

The idea of a canal joining Inverness to Fort William was not new, for geography and geology were on its side. The two towns are joined by a natural fault line running clear across the country: Loch Linnhe bites deep into the land to the west, the Moray Firth to the east. Between the two lies the Great Glen, where the glaciers of the Ice Age carved out hollows that became a string of thin lochs threaded down the river valleys, Lochy, Oich and Ness. The Glen provided by far the easiest route across the Highlands, a fact not lost on the military who soon realised its strategic importance. A fort was built at the western end by General Monk in 1655, and replaced by a more substantial structure in the reign of William III, when it was renamed Fort William. Fort George was established on Castle Hill, Inverness and Fort Augustus in the centre. All three were linked by one of General Wade's military roads between 1725 and 1726. Road building was never easy in the region. The old roads where the line has not been adopted by modern roads are now rough tracks, often occupying narrow ledges cut into the hillside, constantly subject to the hazards of rock fall and land slip, not to mention complete closure by winter storms. In an age when water transport had proved itself to be highly efficient, the string of lochs spread out down the glen offered an obvious and tempting alternative.

James Watt was one of the first to propose a canal in 1773. It was to be a substantial affair, 10 feet deep, which he estimated might be built for a modest £164,000. Nothing happened, in spite of strong local support expressed in the *Statistical Account of Scotland in the 1790s*, whose authors optimistically declared that 'nature has left little to be done'. John Rennie surveyed the route in 1793, but again no action followed, and both the British Fisheries Society and the Highland Society remained keen advocates. Telford was certainly not coming up with an original idea, but once again he found himself the man on the spot just at the time when government was disposed to look well on such schemes. By this time, he knew Watt well, and was quick to acknowledge the value of the work done nearly thirty years earlier. While plans were still being finalised, he wrote to him about his own ideas.[7]

> I have so long accustomed myself to look with a degree of reverence to your work, that I am particularly anxious to learn what occurred to you in this business while the whole was fresh in your mind. *The object appears to me so great and so desirable*, that I am convinced you will feel a pleasure in bringing it again under investigation; and I am very desirous that the thing should be fully and fairly explained, so that the public may be made aware of its extensive utility. If I can accomplish this, I shall have done my duty; and if the project is not executed now, some future period will see it done, and I shall have the satisfaction of having followed you in promoting its success.

When writing his own later reports, he freely acknowledged the debt he owed to Watt's pioneering efforts, a fact which should perhaps be borne in mind when the time comes to evaluate suggestions that Telford was disposed to push his own claims at the expense of others.

Telford, as we have already seen, still had other interests in Shropshire, on the Ellesmere Canal and elsewhere, but it was Scotland and the vast, if daunting, range of opportunities now opening up that completely enthralled him. By early 1802, all the omens looked propitious. The Peace of Amiens had ended war with France – though only the very optimistic believed it could last – and as a result, the burden of wartime taxation had been lifted. If ever there was a time for such a scheme to be pushed forward, this was it. It is not surprising to find Telford writing[8] that 'Never when awake, and perhaps not always when asleep – have my Scotch Surveys been absent', and ending his letter on a typically jaunty note: 'if they will only grant me One million to improve Scotland or rather promote the general prosperity and Welfare of the Empire, all will be quite well, and I will condescend to approve of their measures'.

His personal optimism was to prove well founded, for at the beginning of July, he heard from Vansittart again.[9] His brief was a wide one. He was now encouraged to write a full report on the proposed waterway, already becoming known as the Caledonian Canal, and to consider a new route from Carlisle to Portpatrick, to be developed as the new port for a sea crossing to Ireland. Other proposals included bridges across the Cromarty and Beauly Firths and a transport route from the Great Glen to Loch Duich on the west coast. There was a significant request for him specifically to investigate emigration from the Highlands and Islands, a clear indication that this was to be an influential factor in deciding what projects were to go forward in the region.

Telford duly reported at the end of the second survey, and his views could be summarised under two headings: the Caledonian Canal, and the rest. There was no doubt that if work were to go ahead on the former, it would be one of the greatest engineering works of the age: a ship canal linking two seas and passing through the heart of the Highlands. The rest was certainly not negligible. Telford saw that nothing could be done for the Highlands without communications. Commerce and agriculture could not thrive where roads were wretched, where fast-flowing rivers could only be crossed by means of often terrifying ferries. To get an idea of what the situation was like, one has only to visit the Spey valley, for example, and see the river bounding along over the rocks and imagine the barrier it must have formed before bridges were built. Road improvement and bridge construction were central to the other proposals; there was little point in building harbours if there was no communication with the interior. He remained an enthusiastic supporter for the development of Irish trade from Portpatrick, a view which the government did not share. To balance against that, Telford was equally unenthusiastic about making a canal northward from the Caledonian to Loch Duich. Even if he had not considered the Caledonian itself to be a daunting enough project, the notion of building this branch line through even more difficult country, with all the engineering works that would have entailed, must have seemed absurd.

One element of the report that was to prove crucial was the question of emigration. It is astonishing that although the government regarded the issue as serious, they had no idea of the scale of the problem until Telford reported back. Things were bad and getting worse. 'Three thousand went away in the course of Last Year, and I am rightly informed three times that Number are preparing to leave the Country in the present Year'.[10] It was obvious that the situation was reaching crisis point. The families, many of whom had set out for a new and unforeseeable future in the new settlements and wildernesses of Canada, were just the sort of enterprising people most needed at home to revive the country. Those who remained were sinking ever further into apathy and hopeless despair. Telford was optimistic. He had talked to merchants and seafarers, landowners and men of influence, who agreed that much could be done, and who offered tangible support. If only work could be put in hand, the people would respond to the challenge.[11]

> If, as I have been credibly informed, the inhabitants are strongly attached to their native country, they would greedily embrace this opportunity of being able to remain in it, with the prospect of bettering their condition, because before the works were completed, it must be evident to everyone that the whole face of the country would be changed.

The government was certainly convinced. Select committees were set up to look at four main topics: Emigration, Roads and Bridges, the Caledonian Canal, and Naval Stations. Acting with remarkable speed for government bodies, the reports were ready by the end of June, just three months after Telford's own report was delivered. Two commissions were immediately set up. One was to control the building of the Caledonian Canal; the second, although officially known as the Highland Roads and Bridges Commissioners, also included harbour work within their remit. If Telford had been eager to find work, his wish was more than granted. His appointment as engineer meant that he had just been handed enough employment to keep most men occupied for the rest of their working lives.

In practice, Telford's work over the following years followed no clearly defined pattern. He was constantly moving between his various Scottish schemes and commitments, as well as other projects which also demanded his attention both in Britain and abroad. In order, however, to make a coherent narration out of this confusion of schemes – and a biographer trying to pick his way through the tangle can only marvel at Telford's own expertise – it is convenient to look at the works separately. The first and greatest, in engineering terms, if not in its long-term usefulness to the country as a whole, has to be the Caledonian Canal.

CHAPTER SEVEN

The Caledonian Canal: The Beginnings

Before any construction work on the great canal could begin, there was a lengthy process to be gone through. First of all, the whole line had to be surveyed. There was clearly no problem about deciding the broad outlines of the route, but there were many important decisions to be taken: the placing of locks and bridges, the need for aqueducts, embankments and cuttings, which in turn meant a careful testing of the ground to be covered. Only when this work was complete could plans be put down on paper and costs estimated. These would then have to be scrutinised in Parliament before an Act could be obtained authorising work to begin. This last stage was no mere formality: many canal bills stumbled at the first hurdle, and the promoters had to retire and rethink their plans; some never survived the ordeal by parliamentary committee.

The Caledonian, however, was unlike virtually all other canal projects of the time. In most cases, private companies were formed to raise capital for construction by issuing shares. Some investors were speculators hoping to make a quick profit, a trend that was particularly marked in the mania years of the 1790s. Others were industrialists and traders who looked to the long-term gains that a canal would bring to their business interests. The Caledonian could not possibly have been financed in this way. The mania years had ended, and the dreams of easy money had risen with clouds of ever-increasing costs to disappear from sight. There were no industrialists to profit from the scheme, no traders easily identifiable as eager users for the future. The potential users considered the most important from the first were the fishing fleets – they would be offered a rapid and safe passage between the two coasts in their annual pursuit of the migrating shoals of herring, their main prey, and the Navy, who would be spared the treacherous journey round the north coast, where they were subjected to fierce tides, rough weather and the risk of attack by privateers in wartime. It was also hoped that coastal vessels would make use of the route. Sir Edward Parry, giving evidence for the canal to Parliament, quoted an example of two vessels leaving Newcastle on the same day: the first was loading in Bombay before the second had made it round the north of Scotland to Liverpool.

The fishing industry was still being developed and the Navy was paid for out of the public purse in any case, while the coastal trade was far from certain. If the Caledonian was to be built, there could be only one source of funding: the Government. Today, we are so used to public works being paid for out of taxation, that we regard suggestions of privately built toll roads and bridges as unusual, if not slightly indecent. This is the complete reverse of the situation at the beginning of the nineteenth century, when the general rule was for new transport systems to be constructed through private finance, which could be recouped – or often, sadly, not recouped – through tolls paid by users. So for the government to put up the money was definitely an anomaly, and it is very doubtful if it would ever have been countenanced if it had not been for the panic over emigration. Whether or not the construction of the Caledonian was the best way of using public funds to help the poor and revive the economy of the country is a very different question.

Telford was very conscious of the fact that costs had to be kept to a minimum if government money was to be forthcoming, and he sounded out local opinion, largely through the Highland Society. The landowners were encouraged to think of the large benefits the canal would bring. There were two good reasons for this. The first was that, as he knew all too well from his work on the Ellesmere Canal, a difficult landowner could be a time-consuming and expensive nuisance. Secondly, he hoped that they could be prevailed upon to contribute their share to the necessary connecting links – roads and bridges. Telford had these considerations in mind when he prepared his first estimate. At this stage, the plan was for a ship canal, 50 feet (15 metres) wide at the bottom, 100 feet (30 metres) wide at the top and 20 feet (6 metres) deep, which seemed perfectly adequate for the ships of the time. In order to save money he proposed building the locks with turf sides, a device used on many eighteenth-century navigations, including the Thames and the Kennet. The disadvantage was the loss of water through the porous material, but as Telford argued, not unreasonably, water shortage is seldom a problem in the Highlands. At the end of his deliberations, in his final report, he came up with a figure of £350,000 for a construction period of seven years.

There was very little experience of canal building on this scale. The first ship canal in Britain, the Exeter, had been built as early as 1566, but as it was very short and merely paralleled the river, it was in no way comparable to the Caledonian. Work on what is now the Gloucester & Sharpness Canal was begun in 1793, but was dawdling away at such a lamentable rate that there were few lessons to be learned there – indeed, Telford was to help in its completion, using the experience gained in Scotland, rather than the other way round. The nearest thing was perhaps Smeaton's Forth & Clyde Canal, which was also constructed using some government funding. So it was inevitable that the Government would be particularly cautious, and figures were scrutinised with a good deal of care. It always makes a difference when it is one's own money being considered, not that of someone else.

It has to be remembered that Telford had yet to make his reputation as a canal engineer. He had shown himself to be a man of great ingenuity and spirit, but he had never seen any canal through from its first planning stage to completion. The committee would obviously have relied on expert opinion when considering the plans, but now they were especially cautious. This prudence was reinforced by the experience of so many of the mania canals, where work was foundering for lack of funds, initial optimistic estimates having proved hopelessly inaccurate. It was not then surprising to find not one but two experts called in. The first was John Rennie, an obvious choice, as he had carried out the 1793 survey. Where Telford had estimated £5000 per lock, Rennie put in £14,000, having turned down the notion of turf locks in favour of masonry. He had seen the operation of turf locks at first hand in his role as chief engineer of the Kennet & Avon Canal, which joined on to the old Kennet Navigation. He had also had recent and painful experience of the dire effects of underestimating on the same canal and had felt the sting of public criticism. Those considering the estimates might usefully have borne in mind the state of the Kennet & Avon, which was in some difficulty, and was going to be in a great deal more.[1]

> Mr Sealy was of opinion that the Public had long been imposed upon, by engineers making plausible incorrect statements on the subjects of

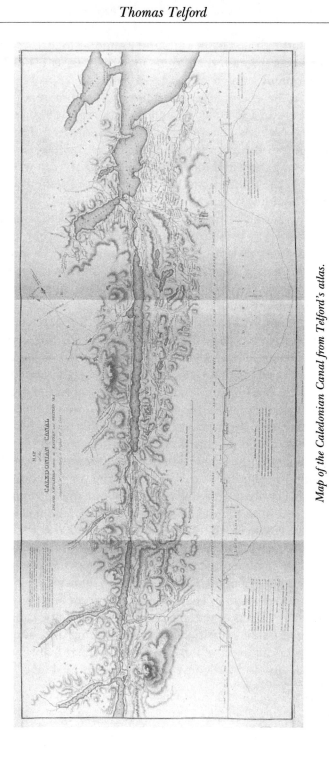

Map of the Caledonian Canal from Telford's atlas.

Canals – Mr Rennie, supposed to be one of the best, had estimated the Kennet and Avon at 400,000 *l.* The money had been spent, and Mr Rennie was again called upon ... The Company was obliged at last to go to Parliament for money to finish it, and it will cost a million of money.

The other engineer was Jessop, doubly qualified as the most experienced canal engineer of the day, who had worked on large-scale construction on the Shannon in Ireland, and had the added advantage of knowing Telford and his abilities. He too favoured masonry locks, but offered the more reasonable price of £10,000 per lock. In the event, Telford was to bow to experience and the locks were to be constructed of stone. The committee was, in any case, convinced of the viability of the scheme, and Commons and Lords agreed to proceed to the next stage of preparing plans.

Commissioners were now appointed to supervise the scheme, and included Nicholas Vansittart and Sir William Pulteney, which must have been very encouraging for Telford. The secretary with whom Telford would have to work on a day-to-day basis was John Rickman. The two men were destined to become good friends as well as partners in great enterprises, in spite of the fact that Rickman was a stern Tory of the old school while Telford had notably more radical views. At Telford's death, it was to be Rickman who edited his memoirs for publication. The land agent, who had the task of seeing to all the complex matters of acquiring land and navigation rights, was James Hope. Telford had nothing but praise for them both.[2] Of Rickman he wrote that 'It was on his able conduct and unwearied zeal and perseverance' that ultimate success depended, and he wrote of Hope as 'an upright professional man, whose only object is the good of all parties in a continued transaction'.

Telford was sent off to Scotland to begin the detailed work of planning the canal, so that an Act of Parliament could be obtained as quickly as possible, and the newspapers carried the usual announcements for interested parties. Government bodies are, however, generally more cautious than their commercial counterparts. The two experts had not entirely agreed with Telford's ideas for construction, and it must have seemed no more than prudent to have a more experienced man involved in the project. John Rennie was a fine engineer – rather too fine, some thought, as they viewed his architecturally beautiful but expensive aqueducts on the Kennet & Avon and Lancaster Canals. Jessop, on the other hand, was widely recognised as a thoroughly sound man, and he and Telford were already proving to be an effective team.

The commissioners took their decision in the summer of 1803.[3]

> Thinking it our duty, in the prospect of so important an Undertaking, to omit no means of enabling ourselves to form an accurate judgment as to the practicability of the proposed Work, and the probable expence of executing it, We took measures as early as the 4th of August, for obtaining the opinion and assistance of Mr. William Jessop, another eminent and experienced Engineer ...

The Caledonian Canal now had two engineers, but who was in charge? Once again, this has been debated, and Charles Hadfield is once more firmly of the view that Telford had again succumbed to temptation and taken credit for work that should be attributed to Jessop. So, the evidence needs to be reviewed.

It is very doubtful if the question of precedence bothered either Telford or Jessop very much. On the face of it, it does not seem that the normal hierarchy applied here. On most canals, the position was comparatively simple. There was a chief engineer who was responsible for the initial planning, designing at the very least all the most important structures himself and laying down general guidelines for routine work. It would usually be only one among many schemes under his control, and he would leave the day-to-day running of the construction to a resident engineer, while retaining ultimate responsibility for all decisions taken. When Telford set off for Scotland he was undoubtedly seen as the chief engineer. But if that was his role, what was that of Jessop? There is no obvious precedent. Telford was certainly not resident engineer. That job was actually to be divided between two men, both reporting to Telford. Jessop's role then seemed to be something quite new, that of a senior consultant engineer. No doubt if a serious difference of opinion arose, the question of seniority would have needed to be addressed. But there is absolutely no evidence that there ever were any serious disagreements, and if there were, they must have been settled amicably by the men themselves, for they are not mentioned in the records. Telford had the highest regard for Jessop; he knew the wealth of experience the older man had gained and trusted his judgements. Jessop, on his side, was a conscientious man, whose main, indeed it might fairly be said only, concern was to see the task completed as well as it could be. At this distance in time, apportioning credit for particular decisions is all but impossible. Telford, after all, built on the groundwork laid out by both Watt and

Rennie. It is, however, quite clear that it was Telford who revived the moribund plans for a canal along the Great Glen, and was instrumental in persuading Parliament to authorise and pay for the first stage of work – and it was to be Telford who was still to be there at the end, even if that end was to come a great deal later than anyone involved at the outset would ever have believed possible. Over the next few pages, the sequence of events will be set out as clearly as possible, and readers can make up their own minds.

It was obvious from the first that Telford was far from averse to co-operating with Jessop, though Jessop was, it seems, busying himself on many projects as usual.[4]

As the idea of Mr. Jessop being consulted was suggested before I left London I was in hopes, if his coming down had been considered necessary, that he would have been here by this time, in which case he would have accompanied me along the whole Line from this place to Fort William, for which place I sett out tomorrow morning.

It is now late in the season for him to examine the Line, and I am obliged to be in Shropshire by the middle of October. But it is possible that Mr. Jessop may not judge it absolutely necessary to view the Line. I can shew him a correct Map of the Line of the Canal, with a section of the Ground; I can describe the nature of the Soil in each District with the situation and quality of the material for Building. He can examine Mr. Simpson an Eminent and reputable Builder, who has examined these matters very carefully, and with whom Mr. Jessop has been acquainted for many years, he can also examine Mr. Howell who took the levels and made the surveys for me, and Mr. Jessop is likewise acquainted with him. If after all this, Mr. Jessop should think it necessary to view the ground, the doing this early in the spring would be more advisable after we have opened some quarries and proved the ground near the entrance to the sea. But if the Commission and Mr. Jessop determine upon his coming North immediately, he will be shown the ground by Mr. Wilson, who will be either at Fort William or Inverness.

Telford, meanwhile, was discovering that working for government was not quite the same as working for private companies. There were bureaucratic rules to be followed, and these rules had to take precedence over such minor matters as getting on with the work. He also encountered for the first time a problem that was to plague everyone actively engaged with the project. Although the money had been approved by Parliament, that did not mean that it was necessarily available when and where it was needed. It must have irked Telford immensely to find himself delayed not by weather, technical problems nor even an inefficient work force, but by the slow grindings of official machinery. His irritation shows in a letter he wrote while waiting for Jessop to appear in Scotland: the intent may be apologetic, but the urge to get on without being hampered by excess paperwork comes through clearly.[5]

> I beg that you will have the goodness to state to the Commissioners that I am truly concerned to find that my not having strictly adhered to the letter of the Instructions with regard to returning copies of my Journal, and as to drawing Bills, should have subjected me in any respect to their displeasure, my intentions having constantly been to promote their views to the utmost of my power. For this purpose, immediately on receiving my instructions, I very hastily arranged my business in England and proceeded to Scotland with all possible despatch, in order to comply with the orders of Parliament, in which regards the Bill to be brought into the ensuing session, and also to provide materials and utensils to make a beginning upon the Basins at Fort William and Inverness during the present Season, so employment might be given to the people and to convince the Country there was a serious intention of proceeding with vigour.
>
> To accomplish this in so short a time, and over so very great an extent of an unprovided country, required that every hour should be employed in the most active exertions. My Journals will show that no time was left unemployed. And if my anxiety to bring the main objects of the business into a train, led me to bestow upon them the time which might have been applied to making out the Journal and Reports, I hope the Commissioners will admit it as a mistaken zeal and to the difficulty of getting an entirely new business of this nature brought into the form which it is both proper and necessary it should be carried on in.

He added that he hoped in future that the commissioners would honour his bills, otherwise no one would be paid and the whole venture would founder.

By the end of October, Jessop and Telford had finally met and Jessop was able to go over the line. They reported their findings in person to the commissioners in mid-December. The final report and estimates were presented a month later, compiled and signed by Jessop. Telford had indicated that he had hoped to have one further consultation before all was finalised, but as before, two very busy engineers were unable to find a time and a place where their hectic lives might coincide, so Telford was sent the report instead. Meanwhile, he was busy in the field carrying out test borings of the ground, and in turn sending his results to Jessop. The two of them did get together to present their findings to the commissioners in February 1804. The job of supplying estimates is normally the work of the chief engineer, as the report forms the basis on which the whole of the works go forward. But, at the same time, it seems clear that there was a division of labour, with Telford busy on the line, fully engaged with the practicalities of getting work under way, and Jessop in control of a fully operational and well-staffed office, able to produce the vital documents.

The details shown in the report were not so very different from those originally envisaged, though the width at water level had been slightly reduced to 90 feet – and it was to change again. Where Jessop had originally proposed a cost of £10,000 for each of the twenty-three locks, a more detailed assessment had resulted in a lower price of £7737. The locks were to be built to what were then the massive dimensions of 152 by 38 feet (46 by 12 metres). By February, the commissioners had declared themselves happy with 'the report and Estimates signed by Mr Jessop' and approved the draft Bill for Parliament with alterations 'proposed by Messrs Jessop and Telford'. When it came to the Lords committee proceedings on 14 June 1804, Jessop gave evidence for the report, and was officially described as engineer, while Telford answered questions on land surveys and purchase, for which purpose he was not unreasonably described as surveyor. Does this mean, as Hadfield has suggested, that Telford's role was entirely subsidiary, or was it the easiest way of dealing with two reports by two engineers? The commissioners quite clearly did not regard Telford as merely a surveyor and agent. Equally, Telford was not too proud to admit that he welcomed Jessop's consideration and experience. Telford made this very clear when he set about the very important task of testing the soil and investigating the materials to be used. He indicated to Rickman that he would very much welcome Jessop's advice. It would, he said, 'be a very great satisfaction to my mind'. As a result, Jessop was invited by the commissioners to return to Scotland to visit the line 'with our Engineer, Mr Telford'. Whatever role Telford may have taken in giving evidence to the Lords committee, his position in the eyes of his employers is unequivocally stated. The work the two men were required to do jointly was central to all future development. The commissioners spelt out the reasons for Telford and Jessop to go over the whole ground again:[6]

that they might jointly inspect the progress of the works already commenced, and reexamine all the particulars of their former Survey; that they might determine the proper situation of each Lock on the whole Line of the Canal, and as far as possible fix the situation, dimensions and construction of the Bridges, Culverts, and other necessary works; and also that they might take into particular consideration the manner in which it would be most convenient to connect the Line of the Canal with the several Lochs or Lakes forming part of the intended navigation, and also settle the price of labour, and the mode in which the several works would be most advantageously lett in Lots to the Workmen, or otherwise executed in the best and safest manner.

All these fundamental decisions were to be made 'jointly'. In the event, a number of changes were made, the most important of which concerned the locks. The Peace of Amiens had indeed proved to be a temporary affair, and the country was again at war with Napoleon. The needs of the Navy suddenly seemed more important than those of commerce, and the lock size was increased to 170 by 40 feet (52 by 12 metres) and the width at the top of the canal broadened out to 110 feet (33.5 metres). The change meant that navy frigates would be able to use the canal. Now that the start was near, key figures had to be set in place. Matthew Davidson arrived, with considerable reluctance, back in Scotland to superintend work in the east, and John Telford – no relation – went to the western end. Each had a salary of 150 guineas plus expenses and a house – for his work in 1803, Thomas Telford had already been paid nearly £700. John Simpson was given the contract for the masonry. Both Simpson and Davidson were, of course, well known to Telford. The appointments were proposed by him and approved by Jessop.

Work on construction was now to go forward, under the joint command of two great engineers, who had been jointly responsible for the plans. Over the years, Telford's role was to increase, but in the first period their payments were remarkably similar: £2464 to Telford from 1803 to 1813, £2057 to Jessop from 1803 to 1812, suggesting an even division of responsibilities. After that, Jessop, now aged sixty-nine, gave up work; he died in 1814. Telford was left on his own to see the work through to completion. It is true that older books have spoken indiscriminately of Telford's Caledonian Canal – and it is well known that when Telford himself was an old man, he tended conveniently to forget the part played by others in his successes – but perhaps it should be clear by now just what was the true nature of the collaboration. It is now time to turn to the equally fascinating story of exactly how the great canal was built.

CHAPTER EIGHT

Building the Caledonian

———————◦▸◦————————

Before describing the canal's construction, it is useful to have some idea of the work it entailed, for it was unlike the majority of canals in that it made extensive use of the natural waterways offered by the lochs. Starting at the western end, vessels make the long passage up Loch Linnhe, which involves negotiating the Corran Narrows, a tricky manoeuvre especially when a high tide is running and currents swirl erratically and in quite an alarming fashion. Then, after passing under the brooding bulk of Ben Nevis, they make an abrupt turn by a little lighthouse to enter the tidal lock that marks the start of the canal at Corpach. There now follows 8½ miles (13.5 kilometres) of artificial cutting, not very long, perhaps, but containing the most famous engineering works of the whole canal. After the entrance locks are left behind, the canal still has to be raised through another 60 feet (18.3 metres) to reach the next level for the approach to Loch Lochy. This was achieved by building eight interconnected locks, where the top gates of the first lock are also the bottom gates of the second and so on, to form what came to be known as Neptune's Staircase. Originally, boats made slow progress up the staircase, as the huge lock gates all had to be worked through hand capstans, similar to those used on large sailing ships for raising and lowering the anchor. To make matters worse, no ship could start up if another was coming down, and vice versa. Even today, when the locks are all power operated, a vessel might have to wait an hour and a half before starting on the journey and allow another hour and a half to complete the passage through the locks.

The mighty leap accomplished, the canal continues over three aqueducts, which hardly register their presence, though they would be considered important structures on other canals, before the Gairlochy locks lead out to the loch itself. Although this appears to be an entirely natural waterway, its level had to be raised by dredging and damming the river, which was diverted into a new course, until the loch was some 10 to 12 feet (4 metres) above its original level. The next short stretch of canal seems quite tame by comparison with the splendours of Neptune's Staircase, yet it represented one of the most difficult problems of all, for the canal had to be carried in the very deep Laggan cutting, hacked and blasted out of the rock. Beyond that is the comparatively small and narrow Loch Oich, too shallow in its natural state, thus requiring considerable dredging. A short section of canal now takes the waterway on to Loch Ness, but not before a steep descent by another staircase, this time the five locks at Fort Augustus.

The deep waters of Loch Ness gave no trouble to the engineers, though at the far end it narrows down to Loch Dochfour, which again needed dredging. The final section must have seemed comparatively straightforward, as it follows the course of the River Ness down the flat valley to Inverness and the sea. But a problem as great as any was reserved for the very end. Unlike Loch Linnhe, the Beauly Firth has a very gently sloping shore. As vessels are not able to approach as far as the coastline, the canal has to go out to meet them. It is pushed out into the bay, with the actual waterway cut into an artificial embankment, before it ends as it began, at a sea lock.

This great work, begun with such high optimism and such zeal when the Act of Parliament was passed in 1803, was to occupy Telford and his men right through to the opening in 1822, a construction period lasting three times as long as Telford had first estimated. Throughout the whole period, he was required to visit the works twice a year and write full reports to the commissioners, who in turn reported back to Parliament. He also had to deal with any problems that might be referred to him. Jessop's visits were limited to once a year. This immense task did not prevent Telford, even at the start, from assiduously chasing after other canal projects, for he was already plotting a canal complex in Leicester and Nottinghamshire.[1]

... the principle is to carry the Canal about 60 miles upon one level, collect the Waste water which falls above this level into Reservoirs and apply it not only to the purposes of the canal but to working Mills for Corn and Manufactories and to the irrigation of land.

This was the notion he had first tentatively propounded in his treatise on mills, and now he felt ready to put it into action. No one could be convinced, and apart from this tentative beginning, Telford seems to have dropped the whole idea very quickly. He had enough to worry about on the Caledonian.

Since one of the main objectives was to provide employment for the local people, as much of the work as possible was put in hand locally. This involved using local smiths to make the simple tools – picks, crowbars and shovels – and local carpenters to make wheelbarrows to a very precise specification and at an equally precise cost of 15s. 2¼d. (76p); somehow one cannot help wondering how that odd farthing crept in. Not everything, however, could be produced in the Highlands. It was important that movement of material be eased by laying plateways of fish-bellied rails for horse-drawn trucks. These were a speciality of the Butterley Iron Works in Derbyshire, and supplies were soon being sent to Scotland together with iron waggon wheels and axles. The waggons themselves were then completed on site in three varieties – side tipping, end tipping and flat trucks for hauling stone. Quarries had to be opened up and masons set to work preparing the stone. Most importantly of all, the Highlanders had to be trained for a new role: no longer crofters and herdsmen, but navvies. By the time the Caledonian was begun, the canal navvy had emerged as a full-time specialist, capable of immense feats of strength. As early as the 1780s, a commentator visiting the Basingstoke Canal had found the jobs mostly taken by itinerant navvies, as local people could not compete physically. With the best will in the world, Telford could not start the enterprise with wholly untrained labour.[2]

> Several people of the Highlands who have been engaged in Canal-work in other parts of Scotland and in England, have begun to work: and they may be expected to prove useful examples to others who have not been accustomed to that sort of employment.

With this nucleus in place, others could be gradually trained up, most of whom had few inducements to move on. The workings were very remote from other canal schemes, and many of the men had their smallholdings which they would return to every now and then, such as at harvest time. Full-time navvies were definitely discouraged.[3]

> The rate of Wages hitherto given to the labourers upon these works, has been about Eighteen-pence a day ... and the numbers of Labourers who

Everything had to be built on site in the Highlands. Telford's notebook contained these estimates and drawings for a simple gravel waggon.

have from time to time offered themselves for work, and demanded a higher Rate, have been uniformly rejected.

Workers on other canals at the time could earn up to 2s. 6d. a day. Critics were later to suggest that Telford had not, in fact, stuck to local workers, and that a large part of the work force had come across from Ireland, a country which certainly provided its fair share of the navvy army. But he was able to show that from the start of work right up to 1819 that the Scots had always made up over 95 per cent of the work

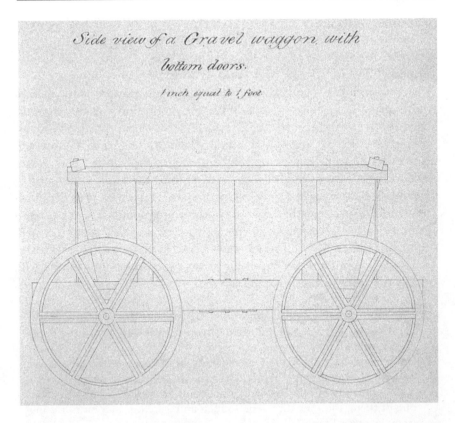

Side view of a Gravel waggon, with bottom doors.

1 inch equal to 1 foot.

force, even when, at the peak of activity, there were 'upwards of four-teen Hundred' men employed.[4] From the start, however, there was the problem of what to do with the sudden influx of workers.[5]

> The accommodation and markets near the intended Canal, and especially at the South-West End of it, are so little adequate to the wants of a numerous body of Workmen and Labourers, that we have found it necessary to continue our attention to their habitations and subsistence; temporary Sheds and Huts for lodging most of the Labourers have therefore been erected; and we have continued in some degree the supply of Oat meal at prime cost ... With a further view to the welfare of the Persons employed, We have encouraged the establishment of a small Brewery at Corpach, that the Workmen may be induced to relinquish the pernicious habit of drinking Whiskey; and cows are kept at the same place to Supply them with Milk on reasonable terms.

If Telford had indeed managed to wean the Highlanders off whisky and on to weak beer and milk then he deserves to be called a genius.

The huts were black houses, crude structures of turf, but as more permanent buildings – cottages, stables and workshops – were erected, the men were able to move into these. Telford had to take responsibility for paying the men. Usually, the government money went through his accounts, and he would make payments in cash, or more usually, in his personal bills, the equivalent of the modern cheque, to the overseers on the spot. At the beginning of construction, the men were necessarily on day wages, not as far as Telford was concerned a very satisfactory arrangement. Inevitably, this was a period beset with difficulties, as he tried to fit the Highlanders into a new work pattern – and new payment systems. He was kept regularly informed of progress by his two resident engineers, and fortunately John Telford's letter book for this period has survived. Both Telfords clearly had their problems. Pay days brought crises at the start, exacerbated it seems by the experienced workers not being happy with either the rates or methods of payment.[6]

> Last Saturday was pay day and a very disagreeable one it was, notwithstanding the men were all informed when you were here that those upon day wages would only receive 1/6 per day they refused to take it, and several of them have not agreed to take their money nor do I suppose it will be settled without going before a justice. Mr Wilson and myself were in eminent danger of our lives yet notwithstanding we would not give way to one of them, tho they threatened much and were on the point of using violence several times.

A week later, he was able to report he was still having problems, partly because some of the men said they spoke no English, but gradually they drifted by to collect their pay: 'those that have since say they durst not take it at the time, it seems to have been a preconcerted Plan'.[7]

But, having got their wages, the local men began to disappear, heading home 'to get their little harvest and Potato crops, and are not yet returned, indeed many of them do not intend to return before Spring never having been used to work in the Winter in this country'.[8] Fortunately, he was able to report that around two hundred were on their way to the workings from Skye, and about the same number again from the mainland, mainly Argyll.

John Telford had many difficulties to face, but he appeared to share with his namesake a certain respect for the country. This was definitely not shared by his colleague in the east who, when he was not grumbling about his health, was complaining about Scotland in general. As John

Telford impatiently pointed out, there was a lot to be said in favour of having one's headquarters in a big town. He wrote to Davidson:[9]

> I am sorry to hear that you are so low in spirits, you should endeavour to keep them up. Inverness is a Paradise compared to Lochaber here we can hardly get anything for money. Mr Wilson and me some time back bought 6 Wedders and put them upon an island in front of the house to graze ... but last Wednesday night two of them were stolen, we are going to kill the remainder to prevent them from sharing the same fate ... there is not a peck of oatmeal in Lochaber, Potatoes is all the food at present Butter 16d per lb Eggs and milk not to be got for money.

Through it all, he kept up a cheery correspondence with Davidson, even being able to make light of a severe gale that caused a huge amount of damage at the workings:[10]

> there was some of the black houses blown down but you may assure Mr Davidson there was not one Highland man smothered, they understand self preservation too well. As soon as the Gale commenced they took to the open shore with their families for shelter.

This was clearly an attempt to cheer up the melancholy Davidson, but when writing to other correspondents, John Telford was rather more open and not unreasonably irritated.[11] He was not a man to make much of his own troubles, and there is little hint that he himself was enjoying rather less robust health than his fellow superintendent of works.

> I suppose Mr Telford has given you a particular account of this country, but if you were to compare his account with Mr Davidson's you would find a material difference – Mr Davidson declared that he would not accept of a seat in Heaven if there was a Scotchman admitted to it ... the severity of the climate puts almost a total stop to all kinds of labours out of doors during the winter – We have here at present about 200 men of one kind and another and at Inverness end there is more than double that number, but that is a very different place from this – there everything may be had for money, they have a market twice a week – at Ft William there is only one twice a year notwithstanding Mr Davidson complains heavily.

However different their temperaments, these two men served Telford well, and the success of the operation depended at least as much on their endeavours in the early stages as on those of their superiors. Yet neither would see the work completed. John Telford died in 1807, his place taken by Alexander Easton. Here, Thomas Telford followed his usual practice of providing a man known to him as solid and reliable – Easton had already worked with him as inspector of roads in Argyll. Davidson, the greater complainer, lived on until 1819, his place being taken by his son, James.

The scale of operations at the Caledonian was quite unlike that on any other canal. As well as the rail system, the company acquired a 44-foot (13.4-metre) sloop to supply the works, which arrived in 1804 to serve the eastern end of the canal, followed by a second for the west, named respectively, and appropriately, *Caledonia* and *Corpach*. The latest technology was now available. Three steam pumps were sent to Scotland by Boulton and Watt to keep out water behind the coffer dams during excavations, such as those at the sea locks. Telford had the problem of getting machines set in motion in a part of the country where such engines were totally unknown. Anxious letters were sent and reassuring replies came from Boulton and Watt. It was normal for engines to be sent with full instructions, and it is clear that these engines were undeniably robust and unlikely to suffer from rough handling. Here is a section dealing with making a piston gasket:[12]

> take sixty commonsized white or untarred rope yarns, and with them plait a gasket or flat rope, as close and firm as possible, tapering for 18 inches at each end, and long enough to go round the piston, and overlap for that length; coil this rope the thin way as hard as you can, lay it on an iron plate, and beat it with a sledge hammer until its breadth answers its place; put it in and beat it down with a wooden driver and a hand-mallet; pour some melted tallow all round; then pack in a layer of white oakum, half an inch thick, then another rope, then more oakum, so that the whole packing may have the depth of about four inches ...

In the case of the Caledonian engines, Boulton and Watt sent their own man, and they were concerned to impress upon Telford the need to give him the necessary authority.[13]

> There can be no doubt that the person who erects the engine house, will be perfectly competent to setting the boilers, under the direction of the engine erector who will be sent for that purpose; and relative to the smith you mention, we may remark, that Scotland is by much the most likely place to engage one in, who should rather be a man of good plain understanding, than of ingenuity, and we are fully persuaded that if he attends and assists in the erection of the engines or some of them at least, that he will be better qualified in mind than if he had visited the south.

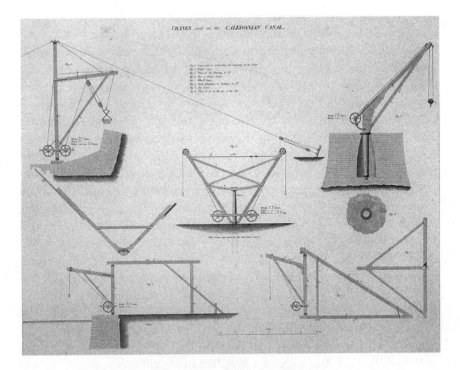

Heavy machinery was a feature of work on the Caledonian – an illustration of a crane from the atlas.

George Taylor was the man sent to the Caledonian, and his first job was to repair one engine damaged in transit. Again, Telford was urged to leave it to Taylor to train up the necessary men who would take over when his work was done.[14]

> We particularly beg to enforce that the propriety of your placing under him from the beginning, the persons who are intended to look after the Engines, that they may receive the full benefit of his instructions during the whole time of erection.

Taylor did his job well, and the engines more than proved their worth. Steam was not only used for what was by then a common task of pumping out water; a new application was found when the Caledonian acquired a steam dredger, designed by Jessop. Something similar had been tried on the Gloucester & Berkeley Canal back in 1796, but to no very great effect. The Caledonian dredgers were the ladder-bucket type, in which an endless chain of buckets was stretched over the frame – the ladder – and then lowered to the river or loch bed. The buckets scooped up the mud and then, as they turned upside down at the top of the ladder, discharged the spoil down a chute into a second boat, which was rowed out into deep water on the appropriate loch. Trap doors in the bottom of the boat were then opened and, as one eye witness reported, the boat then 'bobbed up like a cork'. Telford noted calmly that dredger and barge had both sunk in Loch Oich in October 1806, but pointed out that, as they were not needed at the time, both could stay where they were and be raised when necessary. He might have been less sanguine had it been his latest invention at the bottom of the loch. Steam engines and steam dredgers were at work, and at the peak of activity well over a thousand men were employed. Waggons rolled along newly constructed railways, shanty towns grew up around important sites; saw mills and smithies were kept constantly at work, quarries were opened up, and there were scenes of bustle and activity from east coast to west. Telford had declared as a young man that it was his ambition to be in charge of schemes of great importance. His wish had been realised.

Telford was quick to establish the practice of letting out work to contractors, who were expected to provide basic tools, pick axes, spades and shovels, while the company supplied more expensive items, such as planks and wheelbarrows – though it was up to the contractors to keep them in good repair, and to pay for any that went missing. It removed the problem that John Telford had faced – being personally responsible for a large amount of money for day wages – as work was now paid by measure to the contractors. This could bring its own problems: in November 1804, he found one of the contractors Ewan Gillies moving the boundary pegs to claim extra money. But on the whole, Telford was convinced that this was by far the best system. The contractors were left to set their own pay rates for the navvies:[15]

> but as Canal Work is very laborious, they must ... give such Wages ... as will be the means of procuring and calling forth the utmost exertions of able Workmen; so that although the Wages paid by the Contractors may be higher than those for common Workmen in the adjoining country, yet when compared with the quantity of Work performed, it is by much the cheaper labour.

The following year, he was able to report that labour costs were now £49,242 on measure work, against a modest £5966 on day work. It was very satisfactory, but the problem of acquiring labour never went away:

as Telford noted, the men preferred the comparatively easy work of road building to the very heavy labour of digging the deep canal.

The great work at the western end was the completion of Neptune's Staircase, with its huge amount of masonry work, at the height of construction involving a work force of sixty in the quarries and 120 masons. Work was expected to take four years but was actually completed six months ahead of schedule. Details were given in the 1811 report, and Telford, who, as a former mason, could be presumed to know what he was talking about, proudly noted that 'there does not seem to be the slightest imperfection in this immense mass of building'. No doubt it looked splendid, but in November 1834, disastrous floods and storms saw masonry work collapse here and elsewhere along the canal. George May, who had learned his trade under Telford, was then the canal's engineer, and his report on the failure made some astonishing claims.[16]

> The masonry of the whole structure, judged with reference to the purpose for which it was intended, I cannot characterise by any other terms than that of execrable; a worse piece of masonry than the Banavie and the Corpach locks exhibit is not to be found in connection with any public works in the kingdom.

He went on to assert that the contractor, believing the canal would never be finished, and his workmanship never put to the test, had deliberately set out to deceive Telford. Assuming this was so, and it seems unlikely given Telford's considerable experience, how could the contractor have also deceived the man on the spot, Easton, who was regularly inspecting the works? Telford died before the catastrophe, so we have no means of knowing how he would have answered the criticism. What is not in doubt is that much of the masonry did have to be replaced. It is perhaps unfair to apportion blame when no proof is available, but it has to be noted that serious accusations of fraud had earlier been laid against Easton. He was accused 'of fraud and collusion with the Master Workman in measuring the Cubic Contents of the Spade-Work'. The matter came before the magistrates and sixteen witnesses were called, but when the first six failed to corroborate the charges, Easton was cleared. It did not quite end there, for the unnamed accuser 'entered into a correspondence with some of the workmen at Corpach, whose conduct in consequence became so refractory and insolent towards their immediate employers that it has been found necessary to dismiss them'.[17]

How different it all seemed in the heady days that followed the completion of the canal. In 1819, John Rickman introduced Telford to his friend, the poet Robert Southey, and arranged for Southey to be taken on a tour of all the workings along the Caledonian. The two men got on tremendously well from the start. It must have been a particular pleasure for Telford to have a poet for a companion, and Southey on his part was lavish in his praise of the engineer.[18]

> There is so much intelligence in his countenance, so much frankness, kindness and hilarity about him, flowing from the never-failing well-spring of a happy nature ... A man more heartily to be liked, more worthy to be esteemed and admired, I have never fallen in with.

He was no less enthusiastic about his visit to Banavie.

> We landed close to the Sea-lock; which was full, and the water running over; a sloop was lying in the fine basin above; and the canal was full as far as the Staircase, a name given to the eight successive locks. Six of these were full and overflowing; and when we drew near enough to see persons walking over the lock-gates, it had more the effect of a scene in a pantomime, than of anything in real life ...
>
> A panorama painted from this place would include the highest mountain in Great Britain, and its greatest work of art. That work is one of which the magnitude and importance become apparent when considered in relation to natural objects. The Pyramids would appear insignificant in such a situation, for in them we would perceive only a vain attempt to vie with greater things. But here we see the powers of nature brought to act upon a great scale, in subservience to the purposes of man: one river created, another (and that a huge mountain-stream) shouldered out of its place, and art and order assuming a character of sublimity.

Whatever disasters may have lain just a few years ahead, it was clear that contemporaries regarded this as a very great work indeed.

Southey's casual mention of the sea lock gives no hint that this had, if anything, provided more problems in construction than the impressive staircase. It had to be cut out of solid rock with comparatively unsophisticated tools, using only simple black powder packed into hand-drilled holes for blasting. The material was banked up as a temporary sea defence. Soon one of Boulton and Watt's engines was at work, and after much difficulty, a coffer dam was constructed, based on iron piles driven into the rock of the sea bed. The engine was at work for two hours out of every four, and for four months over two hundred men were at work in the excavations. In October 1811, both Jessop and

Telford were there to see the lock gates hung in place – it was the first lock to be completed on the whole canal.

At the far end, Davidson was equally preoccupied with the other sea lock. Southey found, not surprisingly, that the engineer was still regarded as a 'character' and he was obviously told many stories about him. He summed him up as a 'strange, cynical humorist'.[19]

> He was a Lowlander who had lived long enough in England to acquire a taste for its comforts, and a great contempt for the people among whom he was stationed here; and which was not a little increased by the sense of his own superiority in knowledge and talents. Both in person and manners he is said to have very much resembled Dr Johnson; and he was so fond of books, and so well read in them, that he was called the Walking Library. He used to say, of Inverness, that if justice were done to the inhabitants there would be nobody left there in the course of twenty years but the Provost and the Hangman. Seeing an artist one day making a sketch in the mountains, he said it was the first time he knew what the hills were good for. And when someone was complaining of the weather in the Highlands, he looked sarcastically round, and observed that the rain would not hurt the heather crop.

Idiosyncratic he may have been, but he was undoubtedly a first-class man, and the difficult work at his end proceeded with great efficiency. He had a house close by the present canal office, and the masonry contractors built a block of houses for themselves and other overseers in what is now Telford Street, Inverness. It is scarcely surprising that John Telford cast an envious eye eastwards. The first task which went on with great rapidity was the construction of the basin at Muirtown, to the west of the River Ness. A far greater problem, however, was the construction of the sea lock about 1300 feet (400 metres) from the shore. Surveys had shown that there was a firm bottom, but it was covered by 55 feet (17 metres) of mud. This made pile driving impossible, and as a result there was no chance of building any kind of coffer dam to enable work to be carried out. The engineering solution was to build a huge embankment of clay and stone out from the shore. As it settled, the sheer weight of material squeezed out the mud from underneath, and a firm foundation was finally obtained. This was to be another scene of bustle and activity. One can still see the giant bite taken out of the nearby hill which supplied stone for the workings. Rails were laid as the bank was thrust out, and finally the coffer dam was built and a steam engine set to work, as at Corpach. The sea lock was ready shortly after that at the western end.

Telford had indicated in his initial report that he foresaw very few difficulties in obtaining land and dealing with the local landowners. He had not reckoned on Alastair Ronaldson Macdonell of Glengarry. He was one of the last of the old-style clan chieftains. His portrait shows him in full Highland costume, and he was said never to travel without a full retinue of clansmen. His holdings near Loch Oich lay right across the line of the canal, and he was to prove troublesome almost from the start.[20]

> I understand Glengarry has transmitted a long petition to get the Canal begun in the middle. He wants the money for his land and you may then either make the canal or not. I dare say not ten persons who have signed this petition would work for ten days at the canal if it were begun there. There is employment at the Canal and Roads in every quarter already – and complaints have frequently been made of the demand for workmen raising the price of labour. Why do not the Gentlemen themselves contrive to employ the people to cultivate the land.

Eventually, Telford himself walked over the line with a local surveyor, valued the land and, in October 1811, made an offer to Glengarry, who promptly rejected it. The arguments went backwards and forwards; a second survey was made and the whole case went to a jury to decide. Telford came to know this stretch of land intimately as he went up and down with a variety of surveyors and contractors. The jury eventually awarded Glengarry £10,000, which was a good deal more than the land was worth – almost as much as Telford had originally estimated as needed for land purchase for the entire canal. He must have felt that was the end of it, but he did not yet know his Glengarry. In 1816, the chief brought thirty armed clansmen to drive off the workers who he claimed were damaging his land: he demanded a vast bank to screen his house, called for more bridges than could ever have been used and continued to demand compensation. He was a torment to Telford, but the engineer did enjoy one moment of pure pleasure. The event was witnessed by Henry Cockburn, the lawyer handling the case against Glengarry, and he clearly shared Telford's view of the man.[21]

> The only fearlessness he ever displayed was in an act of madness which Telford (the engineer) and I saw, and to which he was driven by insolent fury. A boat in which he wished to cross Loch Oich, or Loch Lochy, left the shore without him, and a laugh showed that it had done so on purpose to avoid him, on which he plunged with the pony

he was on, into the water, to swim after it. The people pretended not to see, and rowed as hard as they decently could. Telford and others were in ecstasy with the hope that they were at last to be relieved of him, and certainly he ought to have drowned. But after being carried very nearly across (a mile I should suppose), by the vigour of a creature more meritorious than its rider, he got on board, and was praised for what it had done.

Of the other works going forwards on the canal, some of the best descriptions are to be found in Southey's journal, where his obvious enthusiasm rings true, and where he clearly benefited from having the engineer in person as his companion. Official minutes, reports and letters are written by and for those who are familiar with the works, and it is very rare to find eye-witness accounts which give the reader such a vivid sense of what it must have been like to see such works for the very first time. Here he is at Fort Augustus.

Went before breakfast to look at the Locks, five together, of which three are finished, the fourth about half-built, the fifth not quite excavated. Such an extent of masonry, upon such a scale, I have never beheld, each of these Locks being 180 feet in length. It was a most impressive and rememberable scene. Men, horses, and machines at work; digging, walling, and puddling going on, men wheeling barrows, horses drawing stones along the railways. The great steam engine was at rest, having done its work. It threw out 160 hogs heads per minute [8000 gallons]; and two smaller engines (large ones they would have been considered anywhere else) also needed while the excavation of the lower Locks was going on; for they dug 24 feet below the surface of water in the river, and the water filtered thro' open gravel. The dredging machine was in action, revolving round and round, and bringing up at every turn matter which had never before been brought to the air and light. Its chimney poured forth volumes of black smoke, which there was no annoyance in beholding, because there was room enough for it in this wide clear atmosphere. The iron for a pair of Lock-gates was lying on the ground, having just arrived from Derbyshire: the same vessel in which it was shipt at Gainsborough, landed it here at Fort Augustus.

By this time, the whole route through Loch Ness to the sea was open, but there was still a great deal of work to do in the central section. The party moved on to Loch Lochy, and everything Southey saw filled him with a sense of awe.

Here the excavations are what they call 'at deep cutting', this being the
highest ground in the line, the Oich flowing to the East, the Lochy to
the Western sea. This part is performed under contract by Mr Wilson, a
Cumberland man from Dalston, under the superintendence of Mr
Easton, the resident Engineer. And here also a Lock is building. The
earth is removed by horses walking along the bench of the Canal, and
drawing the laden cartlets up one inclined plane, while the emptied
ones, which are connected with them by a chain passing over pullies,
are let down another. This was going on in numberless places, and such
a mass of earth had been thrown up on both sides along the whole line,
that the men appeared in the proportion of emmets to an ant-hill, amid
their own work. The hour of rest for men and horses is announced by
blowing a horn; and so well have the horses learnt to measure time by
their own exertions and sense of fatigue, that if the signal be delayed
five minutes, they stop of their own accord, without it.

There were many systems of this kind in use on canals, the most common of which, the barrow runs, had a series of planks laid up the side
of the cutting. The barrow could be hitched on to a line from the horse
at the top and the man would go up, balancing the barrow as it was
slowly hauled to the surface. On the Caledonian, a more sophisticated
version was in use, as Southey's description suggests. Here, special trol-
leys were constructed with A-frames, inclined at the same angle as the
sides of the cutting. As a result, the platform, which would carry a waggon or barrow of spoil, remained horizontal when travelling up and
down the incline. Even with all the technological help that Telford
could muster, he found that he had to reduce the scale of the workings,
and limit the bottom of the canal to a width of 30 feet instead of the 50
feet of the rest of the canal. Those who pass through Laggan today are
mostly unaware of the scale of the engineering that allows them on
their way, for the banks are largely overgrown by trees. But leave the
boat behind and walk beside the water, and the vast scale of the spoil
banks becomes apparent, and it is possible to look from the top to one
side to see the natural level of the land and compare it with the water
level far below. It is then very easy to share Southey's sense of wonder-
ment.

The canal was eventually opened in October 1822, and the local
paper, the *Inverness Courier*, recorded the celebrations:

The doubters, the grumblers, the prophets and the sneerers, were all put
to silence, or to shame; for the 24th of October was at length to witness
the Western joined to the Eastern sea. Amid the hearty cheers of the

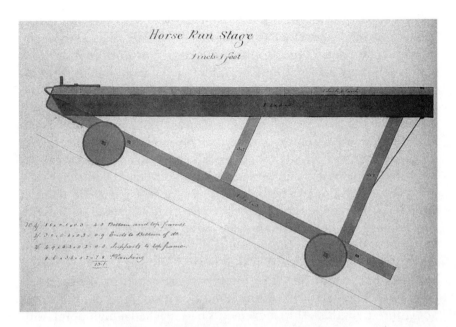

Horse runs such as this were used to lift material up the sides of deep cuttings.

crowd of Spectators assembled to witness the embarkation, and a salute from all the guns that could be mustered, the Voyagers departed from the Muirtown Locks (Inverness) at 11 o'clock on Wednesday with fine weather and in high spirits. In their progress through this beautiful Navigation they were joined from time to time by the Proprietors on both sides of the lakes; and as the neighbouring hamlets poured forth their inhabitants, at every inlet and promontory, tributary groups from the glens and the braes were stationed to behold the welcome pageant, and add their lively cheers to the thunder of the guns and the music of the Inverness-shire militia band, which accompanied the expedition.

The same scenes of wild enthusiasm were repeated at every stop, and on the second day, the official party proceeded by steam yacht to Fort William, where a bonfire was lit. The reporter wryly noted that 'A plentiful supply of whisky given by the gentlemen at Fort William did not in the least dampen the ardours of the population'. An official dinner brought the celebrations to an end.

Elsewhere, however, praise for the canal was muted. Work had begun with much optimism, and in an atmosphere of national fervour. The country was at war with France; there were real dangers to be faced, and the canal was seen as part of the necessary work needed to keep Napoleon at bay. Now the war was over, and it had been ruinously expensive. The national debt had risen alarmingly, inflation had been rampant – and the canal was not immune from rising costs. Raw materials had been more expensive than at first estimated, and land had cost more. As prices of provisions rose, so the wages of the men had to be raised. In the end, the canal initially estimated as costing £350,000 ended up with a bill for over £900,000. John Rennie, the foremost among the trio of engineers consulted at the beginning, was proud in the long term of being the most accurate. Worse still, one of its main reasons for existence had been removed – the Navy, with no one to fight, had no use for it. The Caledonian has often been described as being a white elephant, but some of the criticism comes from being wise after the event. At the start of the century, the sudden leap in shipbuilding technology that saw a change from sail to steam and from wooden ship to iron, with a rapidly increasing hull size, had simply not been foreseen. The canal that had seemed huge suddenly seemed to shrink almost to insignificance. But it was not ignored. By 1835, ship movements had reached a high point, with 544 vessels passing through the canal per annum. It was of real value to the fishing fleet. And there was the factor not so easily measured and quantified: the effect it had in revitalising the life of the Highlands. In that, at least, it was an undoubted success, and as that was the cause dearest to the heart of the engineer who remained with the project from inception to opening, he was content.

Southey wrote a long poem celebrating both the canal and Telford as, in his view, its only begetter. It seems almost embarrassingly sycophantic to a modern reader, and in truth neither the canal nor the man has need of it: the work speaks for itself. The Caledonian Canal remains the most obvious monument to Telford's Scottish work, since it remains the grandest work of the canal age, unsurpassed in scale until the building of the Manchester Ship Canal at the end of the century. We can still see it, navigate it and admire it. It is easy to forget the rest of his work – the roads, bridges, harbours and even churches which were his preoccupation long after the canal was completed. In many ways, these are an even greater monument to his genius and, furthermore, to his capacity for unstinting hard work.

CHAPTER NINE

Highland Roads, Bridges and Harbours

The Government paid for the construction of the Caledonian, and back at the beginning of the century, they had also begun to make money available for roads and harbours. A fund was already available, known as the Forfeited Estates Fund. The estates in question were those taken from the Highland owners after the collapse of the '45. When they were returned in 1784, the owners had to promise to repay all the estate debts that had been settled by the Government in the interim. Part of that money, totalling around £90,000, was earmarked for harbour work. The bulk of the cost, however, was met with new money, and the aims were much as they had been on the Caledonian: to improve communications and to provide work. Similarly there was to be a Commission for Roads and Bridges as there had been for the canal, and an Act of 1806 gave the same body responsibility for harbours. The secretary was again John Rickman, the engineer, Thomas Telford – a very convenient arrangement for both men. There was, however, one big difference between this programme and that for the canal. Improvement schemes had to be initiated locally, and local interests had to provide at least half the necessary funds. Telford was to remain chief engineer for the rest of his life. The challenge was immense, but it was one that he welcomed, and he rose to it magnificently.

Many accounts of Telford's life give startling statistics on the volume of work for which he was responsible in Scotland. He is credited with building over a thousand miles of new roads, rebuilding 280 miles of old military roads, constructing over a thousand bridges, from mere culverts to the grandest of edifices, and more than forty

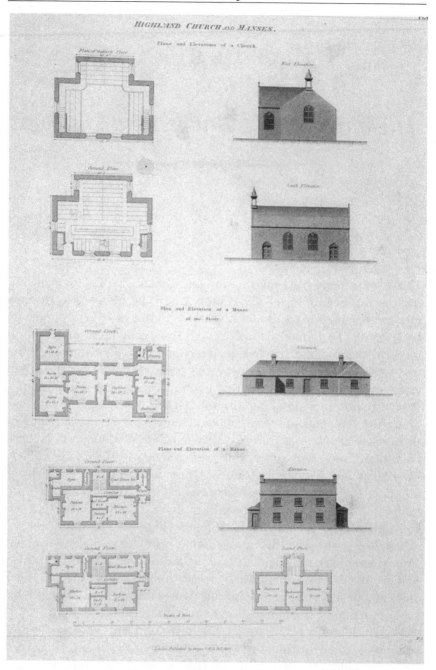

Telford produced standard designs for simple churches and manses for the Highlands.

harbours and piers. As well as this immense volume of engineering projects, he designed churches and manses for many remote regions. It must be obvious that he was not personally responsible for all this work. In road building, he laid out the rules of how it was to be done, and left it to the man on the spot to ensure that work was carried out to his specifications.

Telford is famous for building roads which, though expensive to construct, were to prove of great durability – unlike many roads of the period, which were in need of constant repair. He placed emphasis on two principal factors: good drainage and solid foundations. The best way of understanding exactly what he demanded is to read the detailed instructions prepared for contractors. One of the surviving sets, though not relating specifically to the Highlands, is typical in its detailed specifications and clearly shows his methods.[1]

The instructions were for a road with a carriageway of 30- to 35-foot width and a 5-foot footpath – grander than most of the Highland roads. Drains were to be cut to either side all along the route, with cross drains set at intervals of thirty to the mile. These met at an angle in the centre of the roadway and were to be filled with stone. The most detailed notes, and these are the specifications that lay at the very heart of the Telford method, set out how the roadway itself was to be made. The following quotation describes what was to be done once the necessary embankments and cuttings had been completed.

> Over the whole surface of the Carriage way a coating of gravel is to be laid: it is to be 8 inches deep in the middle, 3 inches deep at the sides of the Road, curving elliptically according to the section. It is to be well screened once, and all stones exceeding 2 inches, in length, are to be taken out. This body of gravel is to be laid on as soon as the forming has been completed, and on the embankments which have become consolidated. It is to be well compressed by carting upon it, and the pits and hollow places are to be kept constantly full by additional gravel at a proper consistency, and uniformly even and smooth surface fit to receive the top dressing of clean, hard, broken materials has been obtained – The same breadth of 30 feet is again to be coated with the hardest of Road flints to the depth of 6 inches in the middle and 2 inches at the sides curving elliptically – They are all to be broken into pieces as nearly cubical as possible so that the extreme points of the longest dimension shall pass through a ring of 2½ inches inside diameter and no piece to be less than One Inch Square.

The footpath was simply made of gravel laid over turf. Nothing is left to

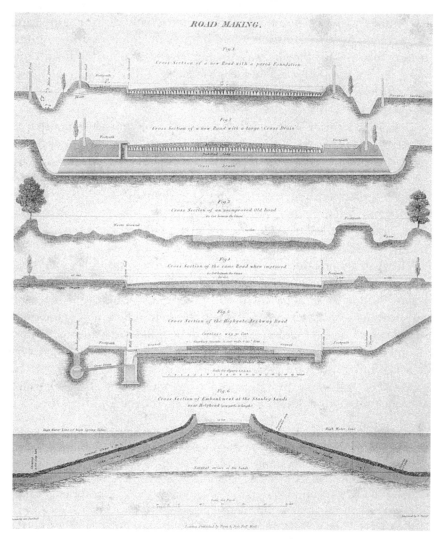

A cross section of a typical well-made Telford road, showing the build-up of the surface and the care taken to ensure good drainage.

the contractor's whim. He is told what types of plant to use in his hedge, and the dimensions of timber to be used for fences. There is, however, a stern injunction that nothing should be skimped and all preparations should be thoroughly carried out.

It is expressly stipulated that the Contractor is to satisfy himself, by his own admeasurements, or in any way he may think proper, as to the heights and depths or any irregularities of other parts of the surface of the ground to be cut down or embanked, as no future, extra, claims, on any pretext whatever will be admitted.

Interestingly, the instructions for building culverts and bridges are given in far less detail. This is quite reasonable. Any competent mason would know how to construct a simple road bridge: it was one of the first jobs Telford himself was required to do as an apprentice. Telford had no intention of revolutionising a design that was cheap, practical and proven by centuries of use. It was only his road-construction technique that was entirely new, and which had to be spelled out afresh for every single contract. All this changed, of course, when it came to major river crossings, and Telford would then set about designing an appropriate structure.

The Highland road works were organised into six divisions, each with its own engineer in charge, under the overall control of the chief superintendent, John Duncombe, who, like so many other trusted assistants, had followed Telford from the Ellesmere Canal to Scotland. The lonely life of travelling through a wilderness, with few amenities and few pleasures – apart from those to be found in a bottle – soon told on him, and his work rapidly deteriorated. Telford wrote in quiet exasperation: 'He seems to be getting into dotage, there is no getting him to finish things in time. I have 10 weeks past stopt his salary and shall pay him only by the Mile, for what he really does'.[2] Telford was reluctant to get rid of old colleagues, but he could not disguise his disappointment, and he could not pretend to mourn his passing.[3] 'I am quite vexed about the old fool – his dying will not be a matter of regret but at a jail at Inverness is shocking.'

Duncombe's successor, John Mitchell, proved an altogether sterner character. A hard worker himself, he expected others to follow his example. He was, as others had been before him, picked out by Telford from the ranks of working masons as a man who had the qualities to take on higher positions. He more than justified the faith that had been placed in him, though his uncompromising attitudes earned him the title of 'Telford's Tartar'. He probably regarded it as a compliment. He was assiduous in inspecting all the work in hand – a task which took him all over Scotland, travelling thousands of miles a year – in a country where there were few roads before he arrived to carry out Telford's instructions. The effort was to tax even his strength and he died in 1824.

Robert Southey, whose descriptions tell us so much about work on the Caledonian in 1819, went on to look at Telford's other works, and he provides a memorable sketch of what it was like to share in Mitchell's travels. His other travelling companion was John Rickman.[4]

> I went back on the S. Side of the river with R. in Mitchell's gig. Had the distance been a few miles farther, I believe neither my poor pantaloons, nor my poorer flesh, nor the solid bones beneath, could have withstood the infernal jolting of this vehicle, tho' upon roads as smooth as a bowling green. As for M. he is so case-hardened that if his horse's hide and his own were tanned, it may be doubted which would make the thickest and toughest leather. But for me – *Pone me nigris ubi nulla campis,* etc. – in short *pone me* anywhere, except in Mitchell's gig.
>
> We returned to dinner so late, that before we rose from table it was nearly ten o'clock.

It was a gruelling day, but there was to be no respite on the next. Southey went off on an excursion by coach down Glen Spean, with Mitchell joining them on horseback. The route they followed is now the A86. After 11 miles they paused to rest the horses, but there was no resting when Mitchell was around.

> M. urged us to go three or four miles farther along the road, which is but just finished, for the purpose of seeing it; by way of inducement, he added that there were some good falls to be seen. He had reason to be proud of the road, which is made with consummate skill and care. Davison was the contractor; an honest, plain, contented man, who works with his workmen, places all his pride and pleasure in performing his work well, and has lost by several of his contracts. If ours was not an *economical* government, such a man would be not merely reimbursed, but remunerated as he deserves – but as things are, he must put up with his loss for his pains. These roads when they are cut thro' the rock, or have the high bank turfed on one side, and are walled up and parapetted on the other, are beautiful works of art; and even when they have no picturesque features of this kind, you cannot look forward or backward upon them without a sense of order, and care and fitness, which is a pleasure of no mean degree.

After viewing the Inverlair Falls, they went on to Roybridge, and then went to see the 'parallel roads' of Glen Roy, which they mistakenly believed to be man-made, but are in fact the shores of old glacial lakes. Southey had an opportunity to see an aspect of Telford's character that was commented on by all who knew him: his generosity. They were staying at an inn in Glen Roy.

When Mr Telford paid the bill, he gave the poor girl who had been waiter, chambermaid, and probably cook in chief also, a twenty shillings bill. I shall never forget the sudden expression of her countenance and her eyes when she understood it was for herself.

The trip also provided an opportunity to compare the new roads being built under Telford's direction with General Wade's military road up the Great Glen. Southey noted that 'he seems to have, like other road makers, followed the old horse track, instead of surveying the country like an engineer', a view he no doubt borrowed from his travelling companion. It reminded him of the old nursery rhyme:

> Here we go up, up, up,
> And here we go down, down, down-ee
> Here we go backwards and forwards,
> And here we go round, round, round-ee.

The road, he decided, was not for the nervous, even if it did offer good views. Southey exaggerated; one can still walk the old military roads of the region. A good example runs along the southern shore of Loch Oich, and while it does have something of a switchback character, it generally keeps to a reasonable line. One other description from Southey describes the road running south over the hills from the Dornoch Firth.

> It is carried 700 feet above the level of Dornoch Firth: nor is there anywhere a finer specimen of road-making to be seen, than where it crosses one dingle on one side, and one on the other; the bridges, the walled banks, the steep declivities, and the beautiful turfing on the slope, which is frequently at an angle of 45, and sometimes even more acute, form a noble display of skill and power exerted in the best manner for the most beneficial purpose. The views over the bay are fine. From this high ground the lake above Bonar Bridge is seen, formed by Shin-Water and Rappoch-Water. The sand and gravel brought to the mouth of this lake by a third stream, the River Carron, have formed the strait where the Bridge is built. We looked down upon the old Highland road, in a part where a little old bridge of one arch over a rivulet, made a subject which an artist would not willingly have left without bringing away a sketch of the scene. On the summit is a point which Mr Telford and Mitchell call Davison's Crag, because when that humourist was met here one day, descending and leading a horse (it was before the road was made, and he was a timorous rider) his knees trembling as much from fear as fatigue, he curst the place and the Crag too, which, he said, had been making faces at him.

'Davison' was Matthew Davidson.

No one can doubt that Southey was genuinely impressed by the works he saw on his tour, nor that this was at least in part influenced by Telford's own pride in his achievements. And he had every right to be proud. He had tackled the task with huge enthusiasm, and had already begun surveys near the Caledonian Canal before the commissioners had issued a single report. By 1803, work had begun on the road up Glen Garry to join the sea loch, Loch Hourn, with Loch Oich at Invergarry and the road running west from Fort William to Arisaig on the coast. On another of his west-coast routes, the road to Kyle of Lochalsh and the short sea crossing to Skye, there is still a chance to see something of the original Telford road by the shore of Loch Cluanie, beside the modern A87. And there, exposed to view, are the layers of carefully graded stone, set down just as the instructions decreed.

How much of the work was actually attributable to Telford himself? He was certainly responsible for laying out the routes to be taken, and he made a point of visiting Scotland and touring the works at least once a year. It is difficult to be precise about these early works, but if one moves forward to the end of his life in the 1830s, there is firm evidence that he was consulted regularly on all major undertakings, and his advice was sought whenever real difficulties arose. Joseph Mitchell, John Mitchell's son, was engineer for northern Scotland, Islay, Arran and Bute. His surviving letters covering the period 1830–4 show him to be very much the man in charge in his own region and, like Telford, proud of what he had done and what had been achieved in the past. He acknowledged that, though his Highland roads could not be built to Lowland standards, change was coming.[5]

> Some of our East Coast Roads, however, have of late assumed the Character of Lowland Roads ... Between Nairnshire and Inverness there are three Stage Coaches and the Mail from Inverness to Tain runs with four horses at the rate of 8 miles per hour; a stage Coach is also about to be started on this line.

As a result, a programme of road widening, surface improvement and parapet building had already begun.

Mitchell was a confident man, but when it came to crossing the bogs of the Findhorn valley in the far north-east he faced a daunting task. He had over two hundred men working in a cutting up to 30 feet deep, and he was concerned over how he could prevent floods, feeling that if he tried to make drains, the stones would simply sink through the moss.

He wrote to Telford, ending his letter: 'I have to apologise for this long letter, but as I feel difficulty about the Works to which it principally alludes I have presumed on your usual kindness to request your advice and opinion'.[6] Telford's reply has not survived, but fortunately Mitchell reported back that he had done as Telford suggested, with excellent results.[7]

> I got the ground drained as you advised, & am happy to report that it succeeded to perfection – After the cut was made to the full depth, we covered the space for the Roadway with two layers of turf, and afterwards laid on a coating of 4 inches of mountain clay, on which it is proposed to apply the Road materials – By this means keeping the drain constantly open, the space for the roadway has become a solid & equable surface, capable of bearing any weight, & that over ground on which it was impossible to stand without planks when the cut was made.

This was not the only occasion on which Mitchell looked for help, and it shows the very high regard in which Telford was held and how valuable his experience was for the workings, even when he could not be there in person.

The roads may not have the visual impact of the best of the bridges that Telford designed, but they are the essential starting point – no roads, no need for bridges. They answered one of the Commission's prime requirements: the roads provided employment, even if the work force was not ideal, lacking the expertise that could have been found in the experienced men who had been used to such work in the south. It was something Telford simply had to put up with, the price to be paid for work that was of inestimable value to the local society. 'In works of this kind, widespread, executed by contractors indiscriminately employed, and amongst a people just emerging from barbarism, misunderstandings and interruptions must be expected'.[8]

But thanks to Telford's careful nurturing of an efficient group of supervisors who could be relied upon to put his detailed instructions into operation, he was to live to see the country's communications transformed. Even so, there is no denying that it is the great bridges that caught the public imagination, and still inspire admiration today. And those who had known what it was like to travel in the north of Scotland before Telford and his men had done their work, were the most appreciative of all.[9]

> Those who are born to modern travelling can scarcely be made to understand how the previous age got on. The state of roads may be judged

from two or three facts. There was no bridge over the Tay at Dunkeld, or over the Spey at Fochabers, or over the Findhorn at Forres. Nothing but wretched pierless ferries, let to poor cotters, who rowed, or hauled, or pushed a crazy boat across, or more commonly got their wives to do it.

In Scotland, Telford felt able to indulge himself a little when it came to design and decoration. His English bridges followed either a very utilitarian pattern, as with the iron bridge at Buildwas, or stuck firmly to the rules of classicism, as at Bewdley. But as he had hinted in his plans for London Bridge, he was beginning to develop something of a taste for the Gothic. It seemed appropriate for bridges in a wild setting, where the only other building of note in the entire district was likely to be a dour, grim fortress. His first important example came very early in the list of Scottish bridges. It crosses the Dee at Tongland, a little way north of Kirkcudbright. Fundamentally, it is a simple, bold design with a single, segmented arch of 110 feet (33.5 metres) spanning the river. The two flood arches to either side, however, are narrow and pointed in the true Gothic style and set a pattern that is followed through in the rest of the detailing. At either side of the main arch are semicircular towers, complete with arrow slits, and the parapet is crenellated to give the whole the vague air of being the approach to some medieval castle. It is the sort of thing that could be comical in the hands of a more rumbustious Victorian designer, but Telford still had enough of the classicist about him to keep the decoration under restraint, and subordinate to the design as a whole. A similar decorative motif was used in the rather grander Dunkeld Bridge, begun in 1806, the year Tongland was completed. Here he had seven arches graded down from a central span of 90 feet (27.5 metres) to 20 feet (6 metres) at the ends. Once again he stuck on mock fortifications.

Among the most impressive works of the period was the road system along the far north-eastern coast. One major obstacle was represented by the crossing of the Dornoch Firth at Bonar. Telford had another bridge planned at the same time, across the Spey at Craigellachie. Both were to be built of iron, so he very sensibly produced designs in which the same castings could be made for both. Each was to have 150-foot (46-metre) arches, but at Bonar two arches were needed, with a central pier on the river bed. Initial tests had suggested that there was a sound rock bottom, but to Telford's considerable chagrin he found that this was not the case. There was solid rock on the left bank, but not on the right. As a result, he had to abandon his invariable practice of always building bridges of perfect symmetry. The main arch was still the 150-foot span, but was flanked on either side by stone arches of 60 feet and 50 feet (18 metres and 15 metres). A stone was erected by the bridge, headed: 'Traveller! STOP and *Read* with *Gratitude* the names of the *PARLIAMENTARY COMMISSIONERS.*' Their names were listed prominently, with in addition in noticeably smaller lettering the name of 'Thomas Telford, Architect'. Travellers did have good reason to be grateful, for a short time before work began in 1811, there had been a tragedy on the same spot, when a ferry had capsized and passengers and crew were all drowned. Southey was told the story about the events and the bridge.[10]

> An inhabitant of Sutherland, whose father was one of the persons drowned at the Meikle Ferry, over this Firth, in 1809, could never bear to set foot in a ferry boat after that catastrophe, and was thus cut off from communication with the south till this bridge was built. He then set out on a journey. 'As I went along the road by the side of the water,' said he, 'I could see no bridge: at last I came in sight of something like a spider's web in the air – if this be it, thought I, it will never do! But presently I came upon it, and oh, it is the finest thing that ever was made by God or man!'

The commissioners themselves were certainly proud of the bridge, and recorded their delight at its proven durability.[11]

> In the year 1814 the Iron Arch sustained, without damage to itself, a tremendous blow from an irregular mass of Fir Tree logs consolidated by Ice; and in the year 1818 it underwent the same sort of probation on its other side; for being situated at a narrow part of the Frith [sic] where the Tide flows with great rapidity, a Schooner was drifted under the bridge, and suffered the loss of her two masts, the Iron Arch remaining uninjured.

Sadly, however, the bridge did not survive the severe floods of 1892, which swept it away. Further north along the same road is another impressive engineering feature, the Fleet Mound. The road rounds the end of the sea loch, Loch Fleet, and is built up over low-lying marshy ground on an immense embankment and bridge. The latter originally had four arches, but at Mitchell's suggestion, after damage by flooding in 1832, two further arches were built and stone reinforcement added to the bank.[12] The road itself continued north all the way to Thurso.

The other great iron bridge of the period at Craigellachie does survive, and one can see just how saddened Telford must have been when he had to discard his original plans at Bonar. The low, graceful arch seems almost as delicate as it does in the Southey anecdote, and how splendid two such arches would have seemed. Craigellachie, however, is quite magnificent enough in its own right, and even moved the writers of the official report to rare poetic flights.[13]

> The River Spey, rushing obliquely against the lofty Rock of Craigellachie, has cut for itself a deep channel, not exceeding Fifty Yards in breadth. Over this an Iron Arch has been constructed, and is the more beautiful, from not being in immediate contact with Masonry Arches, as was necessary at Bonar. The scattered Beech trees and the native Firs on the side of the impending mountain, the meadows along the valley of the Spey, and the Western road of access to the Bridge cut deeply into the face of the rock, combine with the slender appearance of the Iron Arch, in rendering this spot one of the most remarkable in Scotland.

After that flurry of exotic writing, they turned to the more mundane and familiar subject of money. The contractors had worked with enthusiasm and speed, but in the process had lost £500 on the contract. This was not considered unusual. Some contractors lost money through their own inefficiency, others because they had put in an unreasonably low tender in order to get the work. In some cases, however, 'great distress and real hardship' had occurred because the commissioners' own surveyors had underestimated the difficulty of the work, and had refused to make any allowances for the unavoidable increase in costs.

Slightly incongruously, this entirely modern bridge has stumpy castellated towers at the ends, similar to those of the earlier stone bridges. Here, too, there is a plaque, not this time lauding the commissioners, but recording the opening of 1814, and the fact that the parts were cast at Plas Kynaston. There is, somehow, something very pleasing about the fact that the ironwork began its journey to Scotland carried in sections by narrow boat across that other great work, for which the same company had provided the materials: the aqueduct at Pontcysyllte.

It would be tedious to list every one of the major bridges built to Telford's design in the Highlands, let alone the hundreds of minor ones. It is, however, worth recording that apart from Bonar, only one other important bridge has failed to survive. This was the Conon Bridge, just south of Dingwall, an impressive structure in its day built over five stone arches. It was pulled down and replaced by a new bridge, not because of any intrinsic weakness, but because the modern A862 was carrying unusually heavy traffic for the region, trucks on their way to and from Douneray power station. Even here, Telford is not forgotten. By the abutments of the old bridge is an attractive two-storey toll house, built to one of his typical designs.

The road system alone would have ensured Telford a place in history, for the huge benefits it brought to remote Highland communities, but that was only a part of his work for the commissioners. He was also required to carry on the works he had first begun with the old British Fisheries Society, building harbours and piers.

The first important harbour project with which he was involved was the establishment of the port of Wick. It was a natural site for a harbour, with its sheltered bay, and was recognised as such by the Vikings – the name derives from the Norse 'vic', or bay. Telford was not the first to look at the area with the idea of developing a harbour. The Fisheries Society first approached John Rennie in 1793; he produced a favourable report that was left on the shelf alongside his other proposal of that year for the Caledonian Canal. It must have been galling for Rennie, one of the most respected engineers of the day, to have both schemes handed over a decade later to a less experienced engineer, and to find himself ignored. He probably saw a tartan conspiracy at work, and he would not have been entirely mistaken. However, it was to be Telford who produced the next report in 1801 and a much fuller version in 1803, calling for a new harbour for the herring-fishing fleet, facilities for curing the fish and, furthermore, a whole new town to boot.

Work on the new town began in 1805. It was called 'Pulteney Town', a name that brings immediate associations with the elegance of Bath, and the new town in Wick had no reason to feel embarrassed by the comparison. It was, however, to include features which would not perhaps have been very welcome in the fashionable spa town. A kippering house was built in Albert Street, which survives, though unused. In 1806, work began on the harbour, which has been much altered over the years. Herring fishing is a seasonal activity, and the fleets that called in with their catches at Wick might be found a few weeks later perhaps 200 miles away in Fife. An old ruined curing station can be found in the inner harbour where fish were prepared, salted and stacked in barrels, made on site. There were living quarters built into this aromatic building to house the work force, mainly women, who did the work of

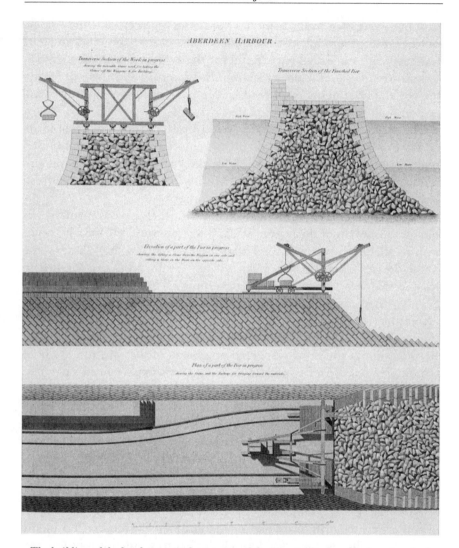

*The building of the breakwater and extension of the pier at Aberdeen Harbour involved
construction on a massive scale.*

gutting and packing the fish and who, like the fishermen themselves,
followed the herring. Sir John Sinclair, the prime mover behind the
whole scheme, wrote a glowing report of what had been achieved.[14]

> Never was money so well bestowed. A scene of industry is here displayed,
> nowhere to be surpassed. Along the eastern coast of Caithness alone, no
> less than 1500 boats go out in an evening to carry on the fishery, and

above 100 decked vessels have been seen in the harbour at once, besides 20 or 30 at anchor in the Bay. Above 200,000 barrels are caught in the season, the very refuse of which will manure several hundred acres of land; a new harbour is nearly completed, the old one being too small to accommodate the number of vessels that flock to it from various parts of Scotland, England and Ireland. Indeed some vessels have come from Cornwall and even from France, and the Hanseatic to prosecute the fisheries here. Nothing is wanting, but the erection of a breakwater at the entrance in the Bay of Wick to render this remote district the great scene of improvement in Europe.

The other major scheme with which he became heavily involved and with which he was to remain connected was Aberdeen Harbour. This was a very different situation from that which he faced at Wick. Telford discovered, as many others had done, that the granite city could be an inhospitable place, especially when the northeasterlies were blowing Arctic air through the streets, and he was led to wonder why anyone chose to live there. He eventually put it down to the Vikings finding it 'one degree less rigorous' than their home land. But he also found a city of 50,000 industrious inhabitants who were notable, as much as anything, for their enthusiasm for education and learning. The port was already busy:[15]

a place of considerable trade, [it] has many conveniences and accommodations; abounds with enterprising and well-informed men; and its being so happily situated between two very considerable rivers, appears to be an object of very great and singular importance.

By securing and extending the pier on the north side of the river adopting a proper plan for managing the two rivers, the canals, the bar, and improving the interior parts of the harbour, of which under these circumstances, it is susceptible to almost any extent, it appears to me that this harbour might be made for safety and accommodation, equal to anything that could be required either for the purpose of Government, as far as regards frigates, or for the general commerce of the north of Europe.

Initially, however, he was only able to work on expanding a project that had already been started by John Smeaton: the extension of the north pier. Once again, he found an admirable man to act as resident engineer on the scheme, John Gibb, himself the son of an engineer, and experienced in dock work. Jessop, the experienced builder of docks, was once again available to provide the necessary expertise and advice. It was clear that nothing much could be done before the pier was completed to act as a breakwater against the fierce seas piling in

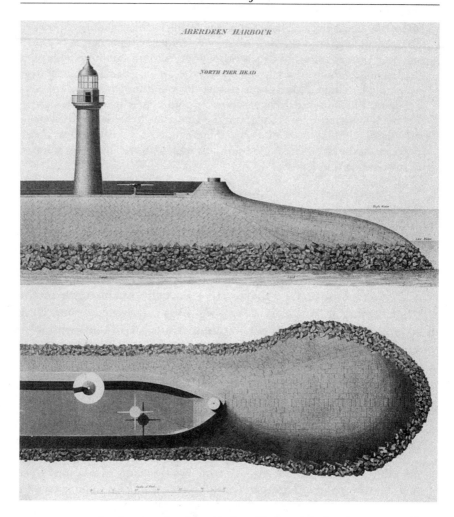

Another view of work on Aberdeen Harbour from the atlas.

from the east, and as it slowly advanced so it proved its worth. There was a frustrating period where everything was assembled for the major harbour work to begin, but nothing was authorised. In January 1812, Gibb was complaining that stone was collected and machinery was ready but at the time all it was doing was cluttering up the pier and getting in everyone's way. Telford suggested that the next stage should be the extension of the south pier and the construction of a breakwater.[16]

Work went on slowly but successfully, and when the north pier was completed the whole harbour had been hugely improved. As work proceeded, the depth of water at the entrance was steadily increased, until by 1828, when the pier had finally reached its full extent, Telford was able to report that there was 7 feet 6 inches (2 metres) at low tide and 17 feet 6 inches (5.5 metres) at high tide. The plans Telford laid out were put into operation throughout the nineteenth century. He was also adviser to the new developments at Dundee, where a wet dock and graving dock were being constructed. The local dignitaries were nothing if not enthusiastic, a circumstance which gave rise to what appears to be the only recorded example of one of Telford's jokes: 'They proposed to build fifteen piers, but T. assured me that three would be sufficient; and in telling me this he said the creation of fifteen new Scotch Peers was too strong a measure.'[17]

Telford was to be responsible for designs all round the Scottish coast and on the islands. Among them all was a scheme which perhaps seemed of minimum significance at the time, but which was to prove one of the most important of them all. He was invited to Glasgow to suggest ways of improving the navigation of the Clyde. It scarcely seems credible now, but at the beginning of the eighteenth century, the river which was to see the launch of some of the world's greatest ships was so shallow that people in Glasgow would often ride across on horseback rather than pay the toll for the bridge. Real improvement began in 1768, when an engineer from Cheshire, John Golborne, was consulted. He appreciated that the root of the problem lay in the fact that the river was, as he put it, 'gaining in breadth what it was wanting in depth'.[18] His solution was to build over a hundred stone jetties or dykes out from the bank. These confined the river to a narrow channel, where the increased flow scoured away the shallows. It worked, but not quite well enough, and Telford was consulted in 1806. He realised that Golborne's work could be improved and that a more efficient system could be achieved by joining together all the dykes with a continuous wall, dredging the remaining channel and using the excavated material to back fill the space behind the walls. The natural river was tamed to something rather more like a canal. It was to prove the starting point for the creation of the great port of Glasgow.

It was also destined to render another of the schemes with which he was concerned at this time totally redundant, even before it was completed. This was a canal that was to run from the west side of Glasgow through Paisley to reach the coast at Ardrossan. The principal promoter was the Earl of Eglinton, who had a vision of Ardrossan becoming the main port on the west coast, with the canal making the Clyde redundant. Telford was called in to give his views, and in 1806, the Act was obtained for the grand-sounding Glasgow, Paisley and Ardrossan Canal. It was destined never to reach beyond Johnstone on the outskirts of Paisley, but that was not quite the end of the matter, for a second Act of 1827 allowed it to be extended by a railway, with a number of long inclines worked by stationary engines. Eventually, the canal was drained and converted to a conventional steam railway, but one wonders how many passengers taking the train into Paisley know that the viaduct they are crossing *en route* began life as a canal aqueduct. As Telford noted later in life, it was not the canal itself that was at fault, but the speed of technological change that overtook it, as bigger and bigger steamers appeared on the Clyde.

Southey has been quoted so often in this summary of Telford's work in the Highlands that perhaps he should be given the last word on this fruitful and satisfying period of the engineer's working life.

> Telford's is a happy life: everywhere making roads, building bridges, forming canals and creating harbours – works of sure, solid, permanent utility; everywhere employing a great number of persons, selecting the most meritorious, and putting them forward in the world, in his own way.

It seems a fair summary.

CHAPTER TEN

The Gotha Canal

——————⫷⫸——————

One might think, looking at the long list of works for which Telford was responsible in Scotland, that there would be little room in his hectic life for very much else, yet just when he was at his busiest he received a letter containing an irresistible challenge. The year was 1808, the project a ship canal that would complete a waterways link across Sweden, uniting the North Sea and the Baltic. The scheme was the brainchild of Count Baltzar von Platen, who, after retiring from a senior position at the head of the Swedish Navy, spent his time actively promoting canals. His first project was the Trollhatte Canal, from Vanesborg at the southern end of the navigable River Gota and on to the sea at Gothenburg, or Goteborg, as it is known in Swedish. Von Platen had a personal interest as the line passed through his estates, and the work was carried out under the direction of a Norwegian engineer, Samuel Bagge.

The idea of a canal that would continue the Trollhatte eastward, by linking the main lakes Vanern and Vattern, was not new, and a survey of the line was made as early as 1782 by two Swedish engineers, Thunberg and Scheder, but as with the Caledonian, such an enterprise could never have been contemplated without public funding. And here Von Platen had advantages, his life in public service having brought him both respect and useful contacts, his position in the Swedish nobility giving him direct access to the king and last, but very far from least, he was a man of immense energy. Once his interest in a topic was aroused, he brought all his considerable powers of persuasion to bear; it needed a strong and resolute character to hold out against Count Von Platen when he was in full flow. In 1808, he talked the scheme over with King Gustav IV, one of Sweden's more idiosyncratic monarchs, who proceeded to issue a Royal Decree, which Von Platen translated into his own, sometimes rather wayward, English. After setting out the proposal to survey and produce estimates for the canal, for which Bagge was originally thought to be the likeliest candidate for the post of chief engineer, with Von Platen to head the enterprise and 'to make his utmost', it then concluded:[1]

> His Majesty Graciously wishes that any of the most experienced Canal Engineers in England, and particularly amongst them Mr. Telford to whom the execution of the Caledonian Canal is said to be trusted may be prevailed upon on proper terms to take a vieu of this undertaking and give his opinion and council thereupon. But, if Bagge should not be able to undertake this performance and afterwards directe the work as leading Engineer, an experienced Englishman must for this purpose be engaged.

Von Platen sent this with a letter, which chased Telford on his busy rounds and finally caught up with him at Inverness, having been forwarded from Shrewsbury via Edinburgh. Telford could never have known just how familiar Von Platen's chatty correspondence would become over the years. It began in typical fashion: 'You will I hope excuse me for introducing myself quite a stranger to You in this manner and I fear in Englisch not of the best sort.'[2]

Von Platen makes it clear that Bagge had already sent copies of plans from the earlier surveys, and it seems that Bagge and Telford already knew each other. It may have been that Bagge had been to the Caledonian works, for one of his later letters indicates that he was familiar with Matthew Davidson and his contribution to the canal. With his diplomatic background, Von Platen knew the advantage of a little discreetly applied flattery, especially when it came complete with a royal name tag.

> His Majesty wishing the performance of this national work to be made in the most perfect manner wich the national circumstances alow has naturaly looked for advices from a Country were such performances are common and particularly has fixed his Gracious attention upon the first of all these performances the Caledonian Canal and his Chief; known by several publications about his work not unknown in Sweden.

(*Above*) Telford in his prime. A portrait from 1812 by Sir Henry Raeburn. (*Board of Trustees of the National Museum and Galleries on Merseyside – Lady Lever Art Gallery – Port Sunlight*)

(*Right*) Telford's mentor William Jessop as he appeared when they first met: a portrait from 1796 by George Dance. (*By courtesy of the National Portrait Gallery, London*)

(*Overleaf*) The Ellesmere Canal turning to cross the Dee valley on the Pontcysyllte aqueduct. (*Flintshire Record Office*)

(*Above*) Wick Harbour in 1865, with the fishing fleet crammed in, while at the dockside the herring are gutted and packed into barrels. (*Reproduced by permission of the Wick Society*)

(*Top left*) The most classical of Telford's bridges, crossing the Severn at Bewdley. (*Worcestershire Record Office*)

(*Centre left*) Another Severn bridge, but this time showing an innovative use of cast iron at Buildwas. This bridge no longer exists. (*Shropshire Records and Research Service*)

(*Below*) The startlingly original design for a new London Bridge, destined never to be built. (*The Institution of Civil Engineers*)

(Left) A steamer descending Neptune's Staircase on the Caledonian Canal. *(Archive of British Waterways)*

(Above) Telford inspecting Highland works in 1819. The gig is being driven by John Rickman's son. *(A. D. Cameron,* The Caledonian Canal, *third edition, 1994)*

Count Baltzar von Platen, the enthusiastic promoter of the Gotha Canal from an oil painting by O. J. Sodermark. *(The Swedish National Art Museum – Statens Konstmuseer)*

The opening of the Gotha Canal, showing the royal yacht *Esplendian* in the sea lock at Mem, 26 September 1832. Painting by Johan Christian Berger. *(The Göta Canal Company)*

It is perhaps curious that such a plan was going forward at such a time, when Napoleon was rampaging through Europe, and Sweden itself had become disastrously involved in the conflict. The king, fearing the spread of French republicanism, had refused to sign the peace treaty agreed between Russia, France and other Scandinavian countries. As a result, Russia had assumed it had *carte blanche* to attack this official enemy of France and had seized Finland. Bagge was Norwegian, and now found his own country officially, if not actually, at war with Sweden. It was then not at all clear when, or if, he would be available for canal work. It was no light matter to go abroad at such a time. Telford replied, accepting the post, and showed that he was as good at official pleasantries as any diplomat when he chose to be.[3]

> I beg leave to state, that I am fully aware of the general importance of the proposed undertaking, and considered myself much honoured by the intimations which his Majesty of Sweden has been graciously pleased to express as to my being consulted. – I am particularly desirous of affording every assistance in my power to the accomplishing so noble and useful a Work and no trifling obstacles or inconveniences shall stand in the way.

He did not, however, regard all obstacles as trifling.

> But these Northern Seas are at present much infested with Danish and French privateers this makes a passage in a common trading Vessel to be attended with a risk from these armed Vessels – however trifling. I must therefore stipulate that I shall be taken up at Aberdeen and also landed at the same Place by either a Swedish or English ship of War – This may be accomplished by sending a vessel from Sweden or applying to the English Government.

This stipulation presented no problem to the old naval man, who went straight to the top by calling in to see the British Admiral, Sir James Saumarez, who arranged for Telford and two assistants to join a convoy heading out from Leith. The last time we heard any mention of Telford's diet, he was boasting of his frugal and sober fare: things seemed to have changed a little over the years. The list of provisions for the three men is now framed and hung, appropriately, at the entrance to the restaurant at the Institution of Civil Engineers in London. It makes for intriguing reading.

Articles for Voyage to Gothenburg

MR TELFORD				to BELL RANNIE & CO.		
1808						
July 25.To 2 doz. Madeira	–	–	@ 75/–	£7	10	0
" 2 " Port	–	–	@ 47/–	4	14	0
" 3 " Cyder	–	–	@ 14/–	2	2	0
" 3 " Piny	–	–	@ 16/–	2	8	0
" 6 " Porter	–	–	@ 7/6	2	5	0
" ½ doz. Gin	–	–	@ 68/–	1	14	0
" " Brandy	–	–	@ 68/–	1	14	0
" pd. for 3 Bacon Hams)	–	–	–	2	8	6
48½ lb. @ 1/–)						
" 2 lib. fim Tea	–	–	@ 7/9		15	6
" 1 lib. Hyson Tea @	–	–	–		11	6
" 2 Cannisters for do.	–	–	–		3	0
" 31½ lib. Lump Sugar 12½ d	–	–	–	1	12	6
" ¾ cwt. Biscuit @ 42/	–	–	–	1	11	6
" 3 Pickled Tongues	–	–	–		15	0
" 5 Casks 1 Case and 1 bag	–	–	–		16	6
" Straw packing and Carg.	–	–	–		6	0
				31	7	0
			disct.	1	11	0
				29	16	0

If it seems more than enough for any voyage, it clearly seemed modest to Von Platen. When Telford was held up by bad weather on the return journey, Von Platen urged him to come back on shore until the ship was ready to sail: 'my reasons are that fearing your provisions of wines and liquors will soon fall short'.[4] After that exchange, one is not very surprised to find that those who came to know Telford well seldom mentioned his preference for water over wine again.

To return to the survey itself: Telford arrived and was met by Von Platen. It is unfortunate that while a huge number of often very lengthy letters from the Swedish count to the Scottish engineer survive, very little remains of the correspondence in the opposite direction. It was, in any case, a somewhat one-sided affair. Von Platen would send off huge screeds full of information and general chat, but often got no reply.

This went on for years, but left Von Platen undeterred: 'I am now determined to write you a letter every week until I get an answer'.[5] And what letters they are. There was nothing in the least bit stuffy about the count, no standing on aristocratic dignity, and a real liking and admiration for Telford shine through. Almost from the first he was addressing Telford as 'Dear Friend', while Telford, on his part, preserved the formality of 'My Dear Sir'. It would be wrong to read into this any suggestion that the warmth of feeling shown over and over again by Von Platen was not reciprocated; it would seem to be as much a question of local usage as anything else. It is quite clear that here was a huge amount of mutual respect, which went far beyond the needs of working together on a major scheme. And it seems that this respect dates back to the very first meeting, as Telford left the ship and the two men set off to inspect the proposed line of the canal.

In some ways, the problems were not unlike those Telford was facing in Scotland. Once again he was to design a canal to link a string of natural lakes, but this time on an even larger scale. The canalised section was to run for 53 miles, over twice as long as that on the Caledonian, and there was a summit of 278 feet (85 metres) above sea level, which was going to involve a great deal of lock building, engineering works to rival Neptune's Staircase. In taking the canal down from Lake Vattern, he had to allow for a flight of fifteen locks, eight of them arranged in interconnecting pairs and the other seven forming a grand staircase. Add to all that the need for deep cuttings through granite as hard and as difficult to work as the rocks of the Highlands, and it was a very daunting prospect.

Telford had the advantage of being able to use the plans from the 1780s, and this was to be the line he was to follow very closely – again, as in the Great Glen, the lie of the land clearly defined just where a canal could most easily be made. He set off along Bagge's earlier navigation at Gothenburg and spent the next six weeks going over the ground. Overall, the journey from sea to sea was 114 miles. He approved the earlier ideas in general but made some crucial changes. First of all, he very wisely decided that, given the terrain, it would have been impossible to stick to the Caledonian dimensions. Where vessels up to 150 by 35 feet (45.7 by 10.6 metres) could push their way through the Highland landscape, Sweden was to be limited to a more modest 105 by 23 feet (32 by 7 metres). Given the huge problems the workmen were to struggle with, there must have been times when he wished he had been even less ambitious. Near Lake Viken, the work

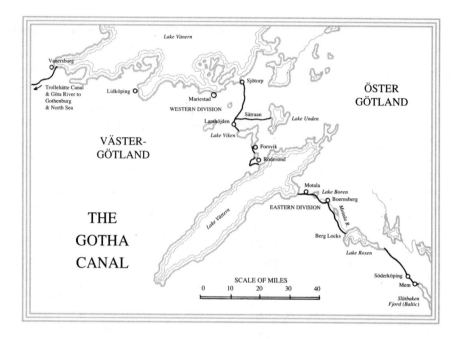

was so difficult that the cutting had to be reduced to 24 feet (7.3 metres) so that if the largest ship able to use the canal came along it would scrape through with a mere 6 inches (15 centimetres) on either side.

Telford spent two weeks at Von Platen's house preparing plans and estimates, and a rapport between the two was firmly established. Reading Von Platen's letters, it is impossible not to warm to the man. One has constantly to remind oneself that this is an aristocrat who had held senior office in government and who was now in control of an enterprise of the very greatest importance. His enthusiasms were quite boyish – he had found a new friend, and a new game to play, and wanted to make the most of them both. Telford, it seems, had left a theodolite with Von Platen, perhaps as a memento of the survey trip, a gift which was treated with self-mocking good humour.[6]

> At looking at the levelling instrument I found I had bettre take a lesson of You about it, than standing talking nonsens last evening up stairs; but as this was not the case Selfinterest should bring me even for this reason to wish You bak for a little while.
>
> Lastly You see mankind are always so foolish either to run away from or run after each other. Now, as in the beginning running away would

not do for our business, we soon found since that it would do neither for our affections; and that's the reason why I find myself always in the habitude of running or looking after you.

Telford returned to Britain, and for a time his part was played. It was now up to Von Platen to see that the estimates and plans were in good order, and he then had to go through the difficult process of getting them accepted by government. He kept Telford fully informed of all the problems, which began with the translation of Telford's report by a Mr Lofgreen: 'After 6 weeks of work I get the most nonsensical rapsodie from him that wass ever seen, I threw it to the Devil.'[7]

Meanwhile, there were political changes sweeping through Sweden. The king was held to be responsible for the debacle over Finland, and he was deposed. Peace was secured, and the new king was actually the former Norwegian commander-in-chief who changed his name from Christian August to Charles August. The changes brought Von Platen closer to the centre of power: he hinted to Telford that the revolution was by no means unwelcome, that he saw the real enemy as Russia, not France, and that his greatest wish was that Sweden would be able to return to a position of neutrality. It was a most curious position in that while Bagge, who had been a native of a nation officially at war with Sweden, was now a representative of a friendly power, Telford officially represented the new enemy. In practice, things were able to go on much as before. Although trade was officially banned between Britain and Sweden, no one ever considered enforcing the embargo.

Eventually, Bagge did come over from Norway, ready to take up the position of resident engineer, not that of chief engineer. This might seem surprising, since he had one canal to his credit, but that had been a very simple affair, and Bagge made it very clear from the start that he fully accepted the need to rely on Telford's greater experience. As he wrote later:[8]

I don't wish to take orders from any man except you or the Baron. It was not for the sake of profit nor for the sake of commodity I did leave Norway, but you know the project has always laid me at heart ... Neither trouble nor reflection should be spared in executing your orders – in short I will be your Davison in Sweden.

The changes in government did indeed strengthen Von Platen's position, so that by 1809, the reports and estimates were officially approved and work could begin. As a recognition of Telford's role in the proceedings, and to his acute embarrassment, he was made a Knight of the Royal Order of Vasa. He declined the honour, but it was too late: what kings have done cannot be undone, and future letters from Sweden would be addressed to Sir Thomas Telford. Much more gratifying to him was the news that work was about to start, and now he was inundated with letters from both Von Platen and Bagge. The former's were the chattier, and so the least likely to receive an answer – a fact which bothered the Count not one jot: 'It would be a very tedious business if in our correspondence I should always wait for Your answer to a former letter before I made a new one.'[9]

Bagge's correspondence revealed just how very much the Swedish work force had to learn about the business of canal building. Not only were the men, who were mostly soldiers, unused to using the tools, the engineer himself had very little notion of just what tools should be used. He wrote to Telford in near despair.[10]

> I most earnestly wish you did succeed in your kind promise to send me some tools and some experienced workmen, especially people accustomed to the puddling process, as it is very little known, and I dare say, there is nobody here ever has seen it practiced, except for myself and it was only for a short time I did see it. Could you also procure us some workmen for the mason work, it would be of unaccountable service, as we are for the most part quite destitute of such people familiar to your mode of building locks.

He tried his best to make use of his own previous experience, and of information gleaned from a British visit, but was very far from being confident.

> I have got some Tools made according to my own fancy, but as your workmen are far beyond in practising such kind of workers I have thought of learning very much from them as well regarding the management of the work as respecting the proper construction of Tools. I therefore most earnestly request your not delaying a Single moment to send us these absolutely necessary men.

The work force then consisted of 900 soldiers, 200 labourers and '150 Russian captives that have defected on the road home being tired of their despotic government'.

Telford did what he could to help. He despatched detailed drawings of locks and bridges, and as samples of basic equipment he sent out three railroad waggons and six sections of rails, three wheelbarrows, three picks and three shovels. It says a great deal about the problems

Bagge had faced that even such basic equipment had to be provided so that copies could be made. Telford was, however, a good deal less sanguine about the chance of persuading workmen to make the still dangerous crossing to Sweden. He reassured Bagge as best he could: 'I have great hopes that you will be able to teach some of your own workmen, in a short time, to perform all the Canal operations.' Telford himself was, as usual, totally committed to his various works in Britain, 'so you must exert yourself and let me have reason to be proud of my disciple, which I have no doubt of'.[11]

Von Platen was certainly appreciative of what Telford could do, while at the same time he was constantly encountering political and bureaucratic bickering at home.[12]

> Please God two or three people of this Country, whose duty in my opinion it is, would show as much care about and I should not experience so many hindrances, so much change and fickelness. Since my last new follys have taken place who without stopping the whole will occasion new changes of plan and Diminution of operations.

Work went forward slowly. Von Platen was able to command a large work force – there were 5000 soldiers spread along the line by the end of 1812 – but what was desperately missing was expertise. Telford did what he could from a distance; but the constantly changing pattern of diplomatic treaties and the swaying fortunes of war made it virtually impossible for him to reach Sweden. Even if universal peace had reigned, he would still have had to fit a visit into a hectic schedule. One has a vision of Von Platen's letters following him on his journeys, fluttering behind him like a flock of migrating birds. One of the flock finally caught up with him in July 1812, and Telford was able to reply to Von Platen, explaining what he was doing: 'I left London earlier than usual, and have been for several months tumbling about among the Hebrides, and traversing the several extensive and rugged N W Districts of Scotland.' He was about to set off down the east coast and did not expect to be back in London until December. He had not neglected his Swedish project, and was still doing what he could to improve the working standards. This time he had sent off several 'working utensils', which he was convinced would be of great use.

> The workmen will do more labour with more ease than formerly, and your country besides the manifold advantages which will be derived from the inland navigation will have to thank you for introducing improved modes of labour, for which the Canal will be the Academy or practical school.

It was all he could do: send what practical help he could and offer encouragement. It was a change in the political world that was to make the big difference. Napoleon's disastrous Russian campaign suddenly made free intercourse between Britain and Sweden possible again, and in 1813, Telford himself was able to return. Now for the first time he could see with his own eyes some of the problems faced by Von Platen and Bagge. It convinced him that Bagge had not been exaggerating – he was really desperately in need of experienced men on the spot. When he returned home, he left behind his two assistants, John Wilson and James Simpson, the son of John Simpson, the trusty superintendent of the Scottish roads. Simpson wrote an enthusiastic account of his impressions, after travelling over the whole route with Telford.[13]

> This Canal is very much favoured with extensive lakes some of the lakes so long as 32 English miles and what is very singular they have rock for all their Foundations, for Locks, Bridges and Culverts, the finest place for a Canal ever my eyes beheld.

He went on to report that Telford had agreed to send two foremen from Scotland and that the Swedish workmen were 'very willing' to be taught. A mason himself and an experienced lock builder, he cast an expert eye over the stonework and declared it excellent, 'although none of them ever had a pick or a hammer into their hands before 12 months last Spring'. Telford's academy was turning out some promising pupils. The lessons were to be continued by two of the young Swedish engineers, Edstrom and Lagerheim, who were seconded off to Scotland for nine months' training under Telford. They seem to have had high hopes of very friendly relationships with the local population, as the list of books they purchased in preparation for the trip included a tome on pregnancy and another on abortion. There is no record of them having to refer to either during their stay.

Things seemed at last to be in good order when, in the summer of 1814, tragic news reached Telford.[14]

> The very worst Canal news that possibly could have happened have reached me here, viz, that Major Bagge in the middle of the Wetter has oversett in a gale of wind in that small boat in wich you went together to the Freestone Quarrie, and has been drowned with all his company: along with him was Mr. North who was now to go over to the west side for to perform the levelling business in company with Mr. Lagerheim and Edstrom; Bagge carried along with him all the counting books for the

west side, several plans and Pappers to be produced at the General Meeting who takes place next month. You will easily conceive in what a perplexity this most unfortunate event put me into at the present and for the future.

Von Platen seemed to be inclined to blame Bagge for the disaster: 'he thought himself a Seaman and realy he was one for fine weather', but did add, 'as for the Canal business he was more to me all respects than even can be filled up by any boddy in Scotland'.

After that, matters began to deteriorate between the British contingent and the Swedes, and it centred on Simpson. He was certainly not very happy with the way work was carried out, and found himself at odds with the military men who were now in charge locally.[15]

> Heare they are very lofty or wishing to be so. I have always found a good friend in Baron Platen and for the others they are very ignorant in regard to Canaling. We are ruled here by Majors – Captains – lieuts. &c. and no person heare is much respected without he belongs either to the Navy or the Armies.

Von Platen, in his turn, felt that Simpson was too inclined to hurry the work, and as his stay lengthened so matters became steadily worse. Simpson was one of those overseers who, in modern terms, wanted to be 'one of the lads'. He went out drinking with the men and it seems was not in any great hurry to pay his way. The result was the occasional scuffle and his fellow British engineers began to distance themselves from him. This was very upsetting for Von Platen, but fortunately he found Wilson's work to be exemplary, which was just as well since he had the most important project on the line: the great flight of locks. In among the Scots contingent was a single Yorkshireman, Ashworth, who was a good, solid worker, though much given to speaking bluntly – 'Yorkshire talking', as Von Platen called it. Matters came to a head in the winter of 1815, when Wilson and Simpson were due to return to Scotland. Von Platen had very decently supplied his own brother-in-law, Ekman, to see them on their way and to show them the works on the Trollhatte Canal. However, when it came to boarding ship, an unholy row broke out. They objected to the accommodation, demanded to go first class, abused Ekman for not arranging things properly, and declared they would never set foot in Sweden again. Von Platen was deeply upset, but blamed the whole episode on Simpson, who had egged on Wilson to join in the complaints. When the news reached Telford, his reaction was immediate. There was to be no second chance for Simpson: 'both you and I have of course, done with him'.[16] Both Wilson and Ashworth, however, were to go on to do more useful work on the canal.

One of the recurring problems that beset the canal was the question of how far it was to be reliant on British expertise and experience, and how much of the work should be used as an opportunity to train up local people and establish local industries. Telford had naturally enough made use of the same basic designs that had proved their worth on the Caledonian. He sent plans for lock gates, of both timber and iron, and iron was also used for bridges. The simplest solution would have been to pass the work to Hazeldine, who would already have had patterns for many of the castings. Sweden already had a considerable reputation as manufacturers of bar iron, which was even imported into Britain for steel making because of its exceptional purity. There was not, however, the same tradition for producing cast iron. Nevertheless, it was decided not to give the job to an established British iron master, but to establish a whole new foundry near the canal. James Thomson, an associate of Hazeldine's, came over from Britain and prepared a site for a foundry, which he confidently told Telford could produce 'all descriptions of cast & wrought iron'.[17] Von Platen was not at all convinced that it would be possible to produce castings as complex as lock gates in Sweden. Nevertheless, work went on. When the foundry was ready, a pair of lock gates was made at Hazeldine and Thomson's foundry in Shropshire, and soon they were not only being copied, but Von Platen proudly announced he was making his own small changes to the design. The foundry was a success in every sense. It proved quite capable of turning out all the work that was necessary, while the works at Motala on Lake Vattern were to develop into an important industrial complex.

The new technology that had proved its worth on the Caledonian was to prove equally valuable on the Gotha. The ladder dredgers had been a great success, and the dredging mechanism for a similar machine was sent over from Bryan Donkin's works at Bermondsey, London, for assembly at Motala in 1822, together with the engines for two paddle steamers. The Swedish works were now in good enough order to be able to supply the iron plates for the hulls and assemble the vessels.

The engineering problems may have been large, but the financial dif-ficulties were far greater. Telford, it seems, had prepared reasonable estimates, but based on the working practices which he had been used to at home. As we have seen on the Caledonian, costs could scamper ahead of estimates with the greatest of ease, and in Sweden, where a wholly untrained work force was organised by inexperienced engineers, they overtook them at full gallop. The burden fell inevitably on Von Platen, who decided that rather than proceeding until the coffers were empty, the best thing would be to make a clean breast of the whole affair in front of the Diet. It was not a happy experience.[18]

> What a damned noise: what an outcry. All the sence and nonsence of the Country at once in motion. It would be too long and tedious to tell you all the particularitys. You are made to such things and I need only to tell You that I have had all the necessary time to remind the different prophecys You at different times and so often have made to me; All sorts of reproaches from all sides, were mercyless thrown out and till beginning of August I have mostly alone been standing in Butt in the House of Nobles. A fine and pleasing occupation when we think ourself actuatet only by zeale for common welfar: But there were two Divil of things of wich people never could get ride, or account for viz. my perturbable calmness and tranquility and the danger and impossibility of stopping so large an undertaking in so many ways connected with general welfar, after it was so far advanced.

In spite of the noise, Von Platen got his way and funds were found, but it was a fight that was to be repeated over and over again as the work crawled slowly and horribly expensively forward. Poor Von Platen – it all made for a stressful life. He ended the letter 'dam them all the have embittered the whole summer to me', though he recovered his old good humour sufficiently to add 'we would have made a fine Banquerupt'. Telford must have been heartily relieved that he only had the engineering work as his personal concern, though he was always ready to offer a friendly and sympathetic word – if not quite so many words as his friend.

So the struggles went on. Many problems never went away. The British continued to have difficulty working with their Swedish counterparts, and the two men who had done so much began to feel the weight of years. In the spring of 1822, Von Platen finally made a journey to stay with Telford, and on his return he wrote a touching thanks to his host. It is worth quoting at length, for it shows how strong the bond was between two men of such contrasting temperaments and such very different backgrounds: the Swedish aristocrat and the Scottish shepherd's son.[19]

> I feel me happy in setting down for to converse an hour with him who along with my wife (who is perfectly well) is my best friend and firmest

support in this world, with whom I have a near contracted so considerable a debt absolutely out of my power to aquite and to whom I own
wholy one of the most interesting and the most instructive and usefull
periods of my life; who only make my regret to be perhaps so near the
term of activite, under wich all I have seen, so can be made use of to the
benefit of my Country: this feeling to wich I must patiently Yield is some
times a little missed with the remembrance of how much and how long I
have been a real incumbrence to You under my long stay; but this You
must in part take as a result of Your own kind invitation of the 29th
March tho' it has not come into my hands before now; and as for me, the
month passed with You will stand highest with me between all the most
common periods of my life; with a warm and unbroken feeling of gratitude, tho, I shall leave of this time endeavouring to express it by words,
as at our parting the absolutely failed me.

That year was also to provide another highlight in Von Platen's life,
when the king made a ceremonial passage down the finished section of
the canal, with a flotilla of vessels including gun boats and the familiar
accompaniment of such events, gun salutes and martial bands.[20]

The only thing missed not only by me but by many others was the presence of you Dear Friend, but I know you are not fond of ceremony. The
king was delighted with the scene ... The two uppermost locks ... were
given your name and the king paid particular attention to the per-
fectability of the work as the result of your aid & I was happy to see this
justice done and am sure you rejoice with me at the success.

It did not mark the end of Von Platen's struggles, and in the very last
letter he was to write to Telford on 18 May 1829, he ended on an
unusually sombre note: 'I have done my duty tho' with little gratitude'. Indeed he had, and when he died at the end of the year, the
canal to which he had devoted so much time was almost, but frustrat-
ingly not quite, open. On 26 September, the great work was complete
and the royal yacht *Esplendian* made the journey from coast to coast.
Telford was seventy years old and did not make the trip to Sweden; the
royal vessel was to pass a handsome granite pillar that marked the
grave of Count Von Platen.

In many ways the Gotha Canal is very like the Caledonian, in that
it, too, has been overtaken by events, but it is also, like its Scottish
partner, still in use and fundamentally little changed from the day
it opened. In many respects, as far as Telford was concerned, it was
the lesser achievement. On the Caledonian he had encountered and
solved immense problems, and been on hand to follow every stage

of the work in person. On the Gotha he had been forced to deal almost entirely through correspondence and intermediaries, with just two visits in all the long years from conception to completion. That does not make the achievement any the less. Indeed, when one considers that the countryside through which it was built was even wilder and more thinly populated than the Highlands, and that for much of the year the workers were faced with extremely severe weather, it could be argued that the Gotha was one of the triumphs of the age. As such, it deserves a high place in the list of Telford's engineering successes. But one cannot help feeling that if it had not been for the tireless and selfless efforts of the count, the Gotha would have been added to that other list which accumulates in engineers' lives, of projects begun but destined never to be completed.

CHAPTER ELEVEN

False Starts and Disappointments

If Telford's road- and bridge-building programme in Scotland, however important it might have been, tends to be slightly overshadowed by the sheer scale and grandeur of his two ship canals, the same certainly cannot be said of his next big road project. The Act of Union had incorporated Ireland into the United Kingdom in 1801, but in practice the kingdom was very far from being united. Communications across the Irish Sea were extremely poor, an inconvenience to many people, including a group who were in a position to do something about it, the Irish MPs. They were able to persuade the authorities to establish a ferry port at Holyhead on Anglesey, to provide the most convenient embarkation point for passengers and mail between London and Dublin. But there was no point in having a new harbour unless one could get to it, and the road to Holyhead was a wretched affair. There were two quite distinct problems. The first was the road itself, which was under the control of no fewer than twenty-four different turnpike trusts, some of whom were conscientious, while others, particularly at the western end, lorded it over roads scarcely distinguishable from farm tracks. The Post Office attempted to run coaches over the route, but with no success. The roads were quite unable to cope with coach traffic, so that the very best that could be managed was to send out teams of riders on horseback to carry the mail. Even that inadequate service fell foul of the truly horrible roads. The superintendent of mail coaches told a sorry tale in which, in just one week, three horses had to be destroyed because they had broken their legs, and in a period of eighty-five days he recorded delays of up to five hours on seventy-one of them.[1] The second major problem concerned the crossing of the Menai Straits, between Anglesey and the mainland. The Straits are notably turbulent, particularly when high tides are running and the water races around the island as it is forced into the narrows. There were many hair-raising accounts of the problems faced by the users of the ferry service, tossed around on the waves before scrabbling over slippery wet rocks to reach the comfort of dry land at the end of the journey. No one could pretend the arrangements were in the least satisfactory; equally, no one had yet come up with a satisfactory idea of what was to be done about it.

The problem of how to deal with crossing the Menai had already received considerable attention. In 1783, John Golborne, who had begun the improvement work on the Clyde, was called in and he proposed two embankments with a lock in between covered by a drawbridge. Nothing was done, but there was sufficient interest to call in Jessop for an opinion the following year. He considered three proposals: Golborne's, a variation on that involving a partial bank, a lock and two drawbridges, and a stone or wooden bridge across the whole Straits. He went into a good deal of speculation about how a bank might affect the flow of water, and the possibility that a changed flow pattern could lead to sand-bank formation near the port of Caernarvon. As an experienced hydraulic engineer, he was well aware that such questions were easier to ask than to answer, and suggested that a bridge might well prove the best solution. Next on the scene came John Rennie, who, in 1801, suggested four possible bridge designs, two utilising the Swilly Rocks and two based on Pigs Island (Ynys-y-Moch). There was strong opposition to the whole idea of a bridge, mainly from Caernarvon merchants who saw their trade being taken away if good access to other ports was established. Again, nothing very much was done, though as a result of this report to Parliament, £10,000 was allocated for harbour work at Holyhead and at Howth on the outskirts of Dublin. There for a time matters rested, until the pot was stirred by John Foster, Chancellor of the Irish Exchequer. He succeeded in setting up a committee to look at the feasibility of building a triple-arched bridge, as proposed by Rennie, and what effect it might have on navigation in the Straits. Predictably, the witnesses produced by Caernarvon all declared it would be a hazard beyond contemplation. But other witnesses did at least give evidence of the dangerous currents in the Straits, particularly around the Swillies where the tide caused severe eddies and turbulence. It was enough to suggest very strongly that the answer was not to build new piers for a ferry service, but not enough to produce any firm decision on what kind of bridge should be built, if any.

There still remained the other question of an improved route from Shrewsbury to Holyhead. Rennie had always had a strong predilection towards imposing engineering works, preferably executed in elegant, classical styles. He had no interest whatsoever in road building. It has been suggested that this was little more than engineering snobbery, but he was then accepted as one of the leading figures in his field, with a sound reputation in bridge building, harbour work and canals. He had no need to add the troublesome and wearisome business of surveying roads through what was still a largely wild and inhospitable country. Telford, on the other hand, was accustomed to doing just that, and had been doing so for years when he was approached in 1810. His brief was to consider what needed doing at Holyhead, to look at ways of crossing the Straits and to find the best routes through Anglesey and Wales, with connecting roads to Shrewsbury and Chester.

It is almost impossible now to comprehend just how wretched the roads were at this time. A Mr Shepherd who walked through Wales at this period described roads which in wet weather became so deep in mud that even a fit man was hard pushed to walk a mile in an hour, and where at the end of the day the best that could be hoped for was a 'filthy bed'. It says a good deal for Telford's stamina and constitution that he was prepared to put up with such appalling conditions in making his survey. He began his exploration from his old base at Shrewsbury. The first part was comparatively straightforward, passing through an area with which he was already familiar from his work as county surveyor and on the Ellesmere Canal. On reaching Wales, he considered two options: one through the Berwyn Hills, along the valley of the Ceiriog from Chirk, but that was discarded in favour of the alternative along the Dee valley through Llangollen to Corwen and on towards Snowdonia. The earlier road surveyors had taken one look at the hills and the stern, craggy mountain passes and opted for the simpler choice of following the Conwy valley to join the coast road from Chester, then heading west through Penmaenmawr to Bangor. Telford struck out on an altogether bolder line, following the Llugwy valley from Betws-y-Coed through Capel Curig into the wild mountain scenery of the shattered outlines of Tryfan and the Glyders, past Llyn Ogwen to the narrow, brooding pass of Nant Ffrancon. The only respite comes as the mountains give way to gentler hills beyond Bethesda. On the final section of his tour, through Anglesey, he met some of the worst conditions of all. Here his predecessors, rather than trying to circumvent the mountains, seemed simply to have tried to ignore them, with alarming results. He found a narrow road with gradients as severe as 1 in 6.5 and in places passing along the edges of 'unprotected precipices'. He proposed a wholly new route.[2]

The most startling aspect of his report was the proposal to cross the Menai Straits by a single iron-arched bridge, the simplest version of which had a 500-foot (152-metre) main span, with stone arches carrying the approach road. It would have needed to be at a sufficient height above the water to allow tall-masted ships to pass underneath. There must be a question mark over whether the delicate-looking bridge could have withstood the severe weather and high winds that funnel down the Straits. The most interesting aspect was the way in which the centring over which the sections of the arch would be assembled was set in place. Telford proposed erecting towers on the abutments at either end, topped by rollers. Cables were to be led across these, so that sections of centring could be winched over and set in place. The system of suspended centring was not actually ever tried by Telford, but it was to prove to be a valuable technique for later generations of bridge builders. No one rushed forward to take up the idea. In fact, no one rushed forward to take up any of the ideas. Telford's timing was unfortunate. His parliamentary Von Platen, John Foster, suddenly found his office of Chancellor of the Irish Exchequer abolished, and he was despatched to a somnolent life on the benches of the Lords. There was no one left to argue for the cause, and Telford's report joined Golborne's and Rennie's to gather dust.

Telford was no doubt disappointed, but not unduly worried. It was not as if he was exactly short of work, and he had another project which he found at least as exciting and of the utmost importance. It had the added advantage that it could be easily fitted into his existing pattern of work in Scotland. It was for a railway to run from Glasgow to Berwick-upon-Tweed. It is easy to see why it would seem so attractive. His enthusiasm for anything that improved the communications in Scotland was still high, and was particularly so when it was seen as this was, to serve the needs of the farming community. And the scale of the enterprise represented a real challenge.

Railways were not new when the plan was put to Telford in 1809, and he knew them well from his Shropshire days. One of the earliest

examples had been built with wooden rails at Broseley over a century
ago. It was typical in that it was built on a slope to join a colliery to a
river navigation. By 1760, Coalbrookdale was turning out the first cast-
iron rails, and soon these simple railways, or tramways, were
developing into useful adjuncts to the country's navigation system,
extending efficient transport to hilly regions where even the most
ambitious canal builder would have refused to tread. South Wales in
particular made intensive use of the system. While canals could be
built along the narrow valleys, tramways were the obvious answer for
the hills that divided one valley from the next. The thinking was very
similar to that behind the canals. There were level sections along
which trucks could be pulled by horses, and inclines, which were the
equivalent to flights of locks, where the trucks could be hauled up the
slope by stationary steam engines at the top. Telford was very much in
favour of such plans, which he saw simply as ways of extending the
usefulness of what he regarded as the most efficient transport system
of all, the canals. There is no evidence that he had heard of experiments on one of those Welsh tramways in 1804, when a Cornish
engineer Richard Trevithick had removed the horse and replaced it
with a steam locomotive. The effects were not felt at first in the world
at large, but in time they were to revolutionise the world that Telford
was creating. If he had known, he might have handed the plans back
to the promoters and walked away. As it was, he was able to use his
report to expound the theory of transport that was to be central to the
whole of his working life. It is therefore worth quoting in full.[3]

> It is, I presume, at this day, needless to observe, that the prosperity of a
> country is most essentially promoted, by introducing the perfect modes of
> inter-course in its several districts. Many parts of England afford such strik-
> ing instances of this, that from the slightest consideration, it will be evi-
> dent that were they now deprived of those advantages, although left in
> possession of turnpike-roads, not only their local prosperity, but that of
> the nation at large, would be materially affected. The transportation of
> raw materials and manufactured goods, and, what is more important, of
> fuel, and manure for agricultural purposes, and the circulating of its pro-
> duce with facility and cheapness, if so limited, or rather rendered imprac-
> ticable on a large scale, would infallibly and speedily lessen the prosperity
> of the State. Turnpike roads, however perfectly constructed have been
> found unequal to the conveyance of heavy substances, where the quantity
> to be removed was great, in a given time. In the best improved countries,
> they are now chiefly employed for the passage of travellers, and for articles
> of traffic, which are of great value, in proportion to their bulk.

The navigating large rivers naturally led early to the improving interior communications by means of artificial canals, and in most situations they are the most perfect means that have hitherto been discovered; but they are limited by local circumstances:- a comparatively great elevation of summit, a difficulty of procuring water upon that summit, its being in a northerly climate subject to be frequently, and for a considerable time together affected by frost, by passing along hills or steep banks, where, although the general longitudinal inclination may be easy and regular, the transverse sections are steep, or where rocks are frequently met with; these circumstances render the execution of a canal difficult and expensive, and the passage upon it, after completed, is so liable to interruptions, as to render it an improper communication, where regular and expensive establishments are by its means to be kept in constant employment.

Under such circumstances, it has of late years been discovered, that, by constructing roads of very easy inclination with cast iron rails, most of the before-mentioned inconveniences are avoided, and that for facility and cheapness, it nearly rivals a canal.

As most of the before-mentioned obstacles, objectionable to a canal are found, in this proposed line of communication; it is evident a RAILWAY is here most advisable.

This was, however, much more than a mere adjunct to a navigation system. The overall length was 125 miles, and even Telford was in need of reassurance. He asked the committee to go to Jessop for a second opinion, as Jessop and his partner Outram were probably the most experienced tramway builders in Britain. Jessop approved, and the plans were duly presented. When the report was put up for consideration, the agent wanted to make it quite clear just how thorough Telford had been and how he had arrived at a final figure for the work of £365,700 – with the almost inevitable ninepence added at the end.[4]

Although Mr. Telford has, with a becoming modesty, said nothing in his report, regarding his own personal labour, and the uncommon attention he bestowed, when he went, step by step, over the whole line of the road, yet it is right, that those who support the measure should be apprised, that there is not a calculation of the minutest species contained in this report, but what was made in consequence of personal inspection, and correct notes taken on the spot.

The ninepence was never spent, nor the £365,700. The whole scheme was simply too ambitious, and the plans were dropped. It never really made sense to construct a route through such thinly populated country. Indeed, even in the wildest days of railway mania, when the steam locomotive had come into its own, no direct line was ever built from Berwick to Glasgow.

This might have seemed a period when he was destined to spend a great deal of time on projects that were never to come to fruition, but one at least was to prove immensely valuable in the near future. In 1814, he was asked to report on the possibility of building a bridge across the Mersey at Runcorn. Telford visited the site and soon discovered a huge problem: although there was solid rock on either side of the river, there were no firm footings to be had in the river channel. He concluded that 'the usual means of Bridge building are excluded, and unless some uncommon one is adopted, the Public must remain without the improvement, which would so facilitate the intercourse between Liverpool and London'.[5] The simplest solution was to build a bridge further upstream: Latchford, on the edge of Warrington, was suggested, where the span was a modest 176 feet (54 metres) compared with around 1000 feet (305 metres) at Runcorn. Telford, however, was not very interested in anything other than solving the big problem, and he realised that the only possible answer was a suspension bridge. Possibly the idea had come to him when considering how he could suspend the centring for his proposed Menai arch bridge.

Telford's notion was to use 'malleable iron worked by wood charcoal', or wrought iron as it is more commonly known, though in Britain charcoal furnaces were rapidly going out of use, and most wrought iron was being produced in puddling furnaces. But, as he openly admitted, he had no idea of the load-bearing properties of wrought iron, what shape of cable would be most efficient, nor how much it would cost. One of the most interesting things about reading accounts by engineers in this period is the almost total lack of statistical information and mathematical calculation. It is true that if one looks at the full account of the building of the later Menai Bridge, there are sets of equations for curves and stresses on suspension bridges, but these were worked out after the work was finished, not as an aid to calculation at the design stage. They were, quite literally, an academic exercise. For Telford, the answer to a problem such as this was to set up a series of tests. There was a well-established practice for testing chains, and he went down to London to a chain-cable manufacturer, where he personally watched and recorded some two hundred experiments, using a Bramah hydraulic press. He discovered that a 1-inch-square rod of wrought iron could suspend a load of 27 tons, from which he was able to satisfy himself that a 1000-foot suspension bridge was feasible. An anonymous appendix to the report gives more detail. Telford had suggested using sixteen cables, each made of thirty-six half-inch-square bars, formed into cylinders. Joints were to be welded, with reinforcing buckles at 5-foot intervals. The cables were then to be bound up with half-inch wire for weather proofing. The annotator adds: 'An undertaking of such immense magnitude, so perfectly original ... ought not to be attempted without the best data.' Indeed so.

Telford soon discovered that he was not the only one with an interest in suspension bridges on the large scale in Britain, though he seems never to have heard that over in America, James Finley had started constructing substantial bridges hung from iron chains as early as 1800. Captain Samuel Brown had begun from the opposite direction, as it were, starting with chains and moving on to bridges. His earliest work was concerned with the use of chains for securing anchors on the ships of the Royal Navy, instead of extremely bulky ropes. He had already built his own testing machine in 1813, and certainly knew a good deal more about the properties of iron than Telford did, even if he knew a good deal less about bridge building. As soon as Telford heard about Brown's work he made contact with him and the two men pooled ideas. Brown patented a wrought-iron link for suspension chains in 1817 and used it on two bridges, one at Berwick, which was to have a very short life, destroyed in a high wind only six months after completion, and the other the Union Bridge over the Tweed, completed in 1820 and still surviving today. Telford was very impressed by the flat chain links and was soon to use them himself.

While Telford was speculating about bridges and busying himself with his various projects, the world at large was going through far greater changes. Napoleon's defeat at Waterloo finally brought peace to Europe, and Telford even contemplated what was to be, if not exactly a holiday, at least a break from his labours. He planned a tour of Europe.[6]

I am projecting a Tour in France and Italy if time can be spared from my various avocations in our own unrivalled and beloved Island. – Indeed my objects are (not of) a very liberal cast. I want to be enabled, from observations, to describe the inferiority of the French and Italian Canals Bridges and Harbours, which from their own Accounts, I now know to be facts; but which from the Rhapsodys of Frenchmen and vapouring ignorant Englishmen have long been imposed on us as wonders of Art and perfection. If they discover my views I shall probably have the honour of being assassinated in protection of the *Great Nation's Claims* to superiority.

It is quite understandable that Telford should not be feeling very well disposed to the country with which Britain had been at war for so long, but there were many French practices which Britain could usefully have followed. The 149-mile (240 kilometre) Canal du Midi was after all completed in 1681, almost a century before the Duke of Bridgewater got together with James Brindley to inaugurate the British canal age, and everything about it was on a grand scale, able to take peniches through locks 98 feet by 18 feet 4 inches (30 by 5.6 metres). As early as 1716, France had established the Corps des Ponts et Chaussées, a body of professional engineers, paid for by government, who soon established a training school for young engineers. Experimentation was encouraged and technical papers written and widely distributed. How Telford would have written about his travels we shall never know, because his work load was once again to receive a massive boost, and ideas of pleasure gave way to the more familiar and horribly taxing and demanding travel on business. It was decided that work should go on in improving the Holyhead Road, and he was required to see to detailed surveys and to arrange for work to begin on improvements in Ireland. His itinerary for 1816 is not just daunting but almost incredible.[7]

I have been and shall still, for some time, be much hurried. After Parliament was prorogued, I went thro. North Wales where about 500 Men are employed, & from thence into and along all the Eastern side of Ireland from Waterford to Belfast & Donaghadee and across by Portpatrick to Carlisle, from thence to Glasgow and back by Moffat to Edinburgh – From thence by St. Andrews & Dundee to Aberdeen then up to the Western parts of that County, then across it and Banffshire – and to every Town on the Coast to Inverness – thence thro' Ross & Sutherland & back to Inverness – from thence across to Fort William on the West Coast & back to Inverness – Then back to Fort William – From thence by Tyndrum & Inverary down to the Crinan Canal in Cantyre, thence back to Inverary – and Loch Lomond to Glasgow. – and again still nearly the same route and back to Inverness – & west by the Crinan Canal and Glasgow to perform over again before I reach the Border. This will give you some notion of my restless life, and, at this Season, a Post Chaise can scarcely render it Comfortable – the Weather here more than half Rainy – and already much Snow on the Mountains.

In toasts, speeches and pamphlets, the two words 'peace' and 'prosperity' make comfortable companions: in practice, they seldom come together with any great speed. The end of a major war brings an immediate time of confusion. Men who have fought in the battles come home; for industries and enterprises geared up to create the machinery of war, demand ceases; and governments which have paid out money for the war find the accounting day has arrived and the debts have to be paid. The situation was grim in the first years of peace, and the burden fell hardest, as usual, on the poor. Low wages and rising unemployment brought widespread unrest that occasionally broke out into riots and bouts of machine breaking. One answer was that which had been estabished for the alleviation of the miseries of the Highlanders: to use government money to fund public works. The driving force was once again Vansittart, who, as Chancellor of the Exchequer, pushed through the Exchequer Bill Loan in 1817, allocating £1,750,000 to be issued in loans to help out public works. Telford was appointed technical adviser for any civil-engineering projects that were to make use of the funds, but more importantly, he was given the go ahead for all the works connected with the Holyhead Road. This included both the new route through Snowdonia and the improvement of the old coastal road, together with the construction of two major bridges, the Menai Straits and Conwy. Plans for gentle excursions through France and Italy were very definitely abandoned. After five years which had seen three important schemes, for a railway and two bridges of a magnitude far greater than anything he had attempted before, apparently lost, he now had sole control over the greatest development of the age.

CHAPTER TWELVE

The Holyhead Road

It is still possible to admire Telford's surveying skills in building the Holyhead Road through Wales, for the route is the one followed by the modern A5. The most impressive section is undoubtedly the road through Snowdonia, which receives a splendid overture with a bridge across the River Conwy on the approach to Betws-y-Coed. This is an elegant cast-iron arch, springing from low abutments. The decoration celebrates two events. Built into the spandrels are the rose, the thistle, the shamrock and the leek, representing the Act of Union, without which the bridge would never have been built, while written right across the arch itself are the words 'This arch was constructed in the year the Battle of Waterloo was fought' – and Waterloo Bridge it remains to this day. Once again the ironwork was entrusted to William Hazeldine, and once again his foreman William Suttle came to supervise the construction – and this time Suttle got his name onto the roll of honour at the bridge.

Once past Betws-y-Coed, the mountains dominate the view. Think of journeys through similar regions in other parts of Britain, and one would think of severe gradients such as those of the Lakeland passes. Here, Telford never used a gradient greater than 1 in 21; a top-gear drive for the modern motorist, an easy trot for the horses of the mail coach. After the glorious elaboration of Waterloo Bridge, everything reverts to the severely practical. Mountain streams are crossed on the sort of simple rubble bridges Telford had used in the Highlands, with no frippery. The scale of the engineering is not immediately obvious, but get just a little way from the roadway itself and a whole array of massive retaining walls come into view. This is particularly evident on the approach to Llyn Ogwen and in the Nant Ffrancon pass, where, apart from the road surface, nothing has changed very much. The road remains on the line and to the same width as it was when built, for the very good reason that there is nowhere else for it to go. It entirely fills the narrow ledge blasted out of the rocky hillside below Tryfan.

Telford's annual reports tell a story of steady progress. The first, of March 1816, recorded that work had begun near Capel Curig, with a work force of between two and four hundred men, most of them, as the Highlanders had been, inexperienced labourers. He was, however, well pleased with how they were getting on in spite of some very bad weather. The following year he was able to review work near Bangor, where 'those precipitous and rugged parts which formerly were most dangerous, are now rendered easy and safe', adding, in passing, in spite of continuous rain and storms.[1] In places the works were now very extensive. 'The new road next passed along the rugged and precipitous face of Dinas Hill, where much rock cutting and masonry were unavoidable ... the Road secured by excellent Breastworks and a parapet'. As usual, trusted colleagues were brought down as supervisors, including William Provis, John Sinclair and Robert Sproat. The results were very satisfactory. Looking back over the road improvements in a later report he described the road immediately to the west of Llangollen as having been 'as bad as it could be'.[2]

> It is a fact that on this piece it sometimes happens that when two coaches meet, both were obliged to stop and fill up the ruts before the wheels, in order to get the wheels out of them to pass each other.

Now, the old, rough, narrow road with its sharp bends and steep gradients had given way to a new road that was 'broad and smooth', and the bends and steep hills had been replaced by easy curves and gentle slopes.

Quite early on in the road-building process it became clear that there was indeed a growing demand for improved communication between Ireland and mainland Britain, with 13,000 passengers a year going through Holyhead by 1818. So Telford was given an expanded task: to supervise the improvements over the English section of the road. This was a real chore, with none of the glamour and excitement of pushing new routes through wild, mountainous scenery. He set off on what he called, in an unusually and gloomy note for him, the 'laborious and tedious' task of going over the whole route between London and Chirk.

It was also an unhappy experience. The bald statement of what he had done sounds well enough:[3]

> The whole of the present Road, a distance of about 178 miles, has now been carefully Surveyed and accurately laid down in proper Maps and Sections. I have compared these with the ground, and obtained data to enable me to report thereon – many of the necessary variations and improvements have also been surveyed.

What was detailed later was a sorry catalogue of inadequacies: roads which were nominally the right width, but on which only the central section could take a carriage while the rest was soft, gooey mud; narrow roads; steep roads; roads built lower than the surrounding fields so that they acted as drains; and so the list goes on. At the root of it all was the system of control by a dispiritingly large number of separate trusts, some of them ludicrously small, such as the Hockliffe Trust, responsible for a derisory four-and-a-half miles. No wonder Telford noted that 'the multiplicity of opinions and directions tends to perplex the Surveyors'. His solution was to scrap this system in favour of the one used so successfully in canal work, where a committee was set up to control the whole enterprise, and the actual work was let out to contractors. The surveyor would no longer have to employ direct labour, and their contractors could gradually build up an experienced work force. Nothing happened, and five years later he was still facing individual trusts.

In his report of that year,[4] he singled out a number of trusts whose work was seriously below standard. The section controlled by the St Albans Trust, for example, was in dreadful condition, so badly maintained that, each autumn, water went straight through the top surface until it reached clay, where it collected until the whole was soon a morass, with a surface 'like glue', and at times the carriage wheels could only be turned at all by 'the severe labour of the horses'. Add to that 'a succession of severe bends and windings', and it is easy to see why at times Telford must have wondered if the whole road would ever be brought up to standard. He patiently reiterated his proposals for a change in the system. He knew, he declared, that the idea of the trusts looked good in theory. The work of maintaining the roads went to local people who had an interest in seeing the job well done, but in practice the whole thing collapsed under the weight of petty disputes and jealousies. It was not specifically a question of finance and resources. The Wednesbury Trust, for example, had adequate funds and easy access to a supply of first-rate raw material, but the organisation was lacking. As a result, the road was 'in as bad a condition as it is possible for a road to be, without actually being broken into deep holes'. It was all very frustrating, but the work continued in spite of the difficulties.

When reading Telford's reports it is impossible not to sympathise with him. He was dealing with a route stretching for over 300 miles, counting in the Chester road, and it was difficult to make a body responsible for the 4 miles outside their own back door appreciate their part in the wider scheme. But he battled on, and no detail was too small for his attention. He produced standard designs for toll houses, with detailed specifications, right down to which rooms were to be floored with tiles and which were to have floorboards, and even the wood to be used. He designed the toll gates, not dissimilar in style to the later 'sun burst' pattern of Art Deco. Milestones were provided all along the route, with cast-iron plates set into stone blocks. His chief concern, however, was first and foremost the nature of the roadway itself. Typical specifications have already been given (see pp. 103–5) and similar standards applied throughout the route to Holyhead, and on the short extension that linked Dublin to its port. His methods did not come cheap. Detailed costings from the parliamentary commissioners for the period from 1815 to 1830 showed, for example, expenditure on the road between Shrewsbury and Bangor of £135,249 and £41,201 for the route through Anglesey. Dear they may have been, but Telford also gave good value: his roads were built to last.

Telford was not, of course, the only road builder at work in the period, and although there was no other single project comparable to the Holyhead Road, work was going on throughout the country through the numerous turnpike trusts which Telford so disliked. Prominent among the other road engineers was Telford's contemporary John Loudon McAdam (1756–1836), a fellow Scot, but one brought up largely in America where he made a personal fortune, some £10,000 of which he was personally to invest in road improvement. Telford's method of building was very similar to that first used in France in the 1770s by Pierre Trésaguet, and with his diligence in collecting information, Telford must have had some notion of what was going on across the Channel, however much he might have derided French achievements later. McAdam, however, used a different system. He believed that there was no need for a solid stone foundation, but that earth was perfectly adequate, with the very important proviso that it had to be kept dry. It is best explained in his own words.[5]

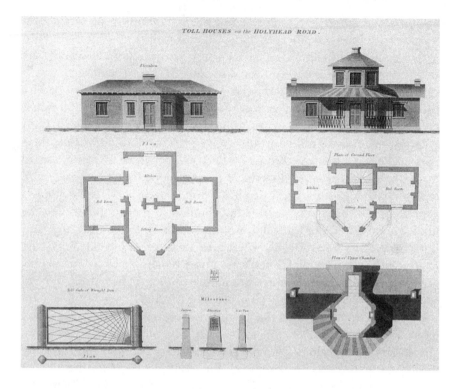

The standard designs for toll houses and toll gates on the Holyhead Road.

As no artificial road can be made so good as the natural soil in a *dry state*, it is necessary to preserve this state. The first operation should be the reverse of digging a trench. The road should not be sunk below, but raised above, the adjacent ground; that there be a sufficient fall to take off the water, so that it should be some inches below the level of the ground upon which the road is, either by making the drains to lower ground or, if that be not practicable from the nature of the country, then the soil upon which the road is to be laid, must be raised some inches above the level of the water.

Having secured the soil from *under* water, the road-maker is next to secure it from rain water, by a solid road, of clean, dry stone, or flint, so selected, prepared and laid, as to be impervious to water; and this cannot be effected, unless the greatest care be taken, that no earth, clay, chalk, or other matter, that will hold water, be mixed with the broken stone; which must be so laid, as to unite by its own angles into a firm, compact, impenetrable body.

The thickness of such a road is immaterial; as to its strength for carrying weight, this object is obtained by a dry surface, over which the road is to be placed as a covering, to preserve it in that state: experience having shewn, that if water passes through a road and fills the native soil, the road, whatever its thickness, loses its support and goes to pieces.

The McAdam system was much cheaper than Telford's and was considered very favourably by many authorities because the job of preparing the small stones could be given to women and children, which was thought a great advantage to the poor – as well as a further cost saving to the employer. A McAdam road was not as durable as a Telford, but it was quite adequate and enabled a huge improvement to be made in the country's road system at a price which most turnpike trusts could afford. At one time McAdam was said to be employing three hundred junior surveyors all over Britain. Historians have argued over who was the 'better' road builder, and there is no doubt that in his own lifetime McAdam attracted criticism. He did not set himself up as an engineer: he was a businessman whose business happened to be making roads. In essence this would have given him the standing of a large contractor, if he had not been making roads to his own design. So, much of the criticism – that he was making a lot of money and employing his own family – is irrelevant. That did not stop critics attacking when parliamentary profits were under discussion.[6]

> Mr Macadam in bringing the system into general operation was entitled to reward. Mr. Macadam's sense of private advantage had led him and three of his sons to embark in an object: the success that had attended their speculation had granted them all the most liberal remuneration. Out of different public trusts for the last five years they had drawn no less sum than £41,000. Their claim for expenses on the average of £400 per annum for each of the family was made not on the economical rate of a surveyor of the road – who would have been satisfied to ride on his horse and live on a beefsteak or mutton chop. The family of Macadam travelled in their postchaise and enjoyed all the delicacies of the season.

The implication that McAdam was pursuing personal gain while Telford was acting as a disinterested party, working only for the public good, is nonsensical. Both men received considerable fees which they earned for outstanding work. Both contributed immensely to building up a sound transport system in Britain. Telford's work was appropriate for the highly prestigious mail route, McAdam's more than adequate for other roads which often had to be paid for out of limited funds. Robert Southey punningly dubbed Thomas Telford 'The

Colossus of Roads'. The name could just appropriately have been applied to McAdam. But if they can be accorded equal status as road builders, it always has to be remembered that Telford had many more claims to fame. The Holyhead Road was also to show his engineering work at its finest.

The grandest and certainly the most important bridge he ever built was his suspension bridge over the Menai Straits. Approval to go ahead with the bridge was received in 1817, and by February 1818 the plans were ready. The design of the suspension chains owed something to Brown and something to his own earlier experiments for the Runcorn bridge. He proposed using sixteen chains, each constructed of half-inch-square iron bars, welded together and secured by buckles. Brown, meanwhile, was at work on his bridges on the Scottish border and would be able to claim the honour of designing the first completed suspension bridge in Britain, but on a scale that was in no way comparable to the immense scheme going forward in Wales. Here, a settlement was being formed, with barracks for the workmen, temporary workshops and a newly constructed lime kiln. By mid-1818, a schooner and a flat, a local form of barge, had been purchased to bring stone and ironwork to the site and quarries had been opened up. Even at this late stage, the Caernarvon interest was still trying to raise opposition to the bridge, while the Marquis of Anglesey, in a fine example of public-spirited enthusiasm, complained that it would disturb his privacy. Some objectors at least did well out of the enquiry. Miss Williams, who had inherited the rights to run the ferry, first bestowed on one of her ancestors by Elizabeth I, received £26,557 compensation, a considerable dowry which acquired her an aristocratic husband in Sir David Erskine. The opposition was finally quashed when Parliament gave official approval to the scheme through a special Bill.

Fortunately, one of the key men on the spot, the resident engineer, William Provis, wrote a full account of every stage of construction of the great work.[7] And what an immense work it turned out to be, with dangers and obstacles present at every stage. One of the greatest problems highlighted just why the bridge was needed in the first place. Most construction materials came by water, and in the heavy storm of 1820, the schooner was all but wrecked in the Straits and two other smaller vessels seriously damaged. Nevertheless, work went on, and the old Telford team was reassembled with such seasoned players as John Wilson from the Caledonian to look after masonry work, while

Thomas Rhodes, who had worked with Matthew Davidson, was to be responsible for erecting the ironwork sent down from – need one say – Hazeldine.

The first stage involved the erection of the two massive pyramidal towers that were to support the chains. The Ynys-y-Moch rocks had to be levelled at the Anglesey end for the southern tower, and an approach road constructed at either end, carried on three stone arches, each with a 52½-foot (16-metre) span. That left a suspended central span that dwarfed anything ever attempted by bridge builders, stretching for 579 feet (176.5 metres) and rising 100 feet (30.5 metres) above the water.

One of the secrets of the success of the whole operation lay in its efficient organisation. Before work began on the Anglesey tower, a temporary platform was built out to the rocks, and railed tracks laid for the waggons. Shear legs were erected to unload stone from the trucks, and smaller cranes were then used to raise the blocks of stone until the 153-foot (46.6-metre) towers were completed. The stonework alone was on as grand a scale as anything that Telford had ever attempted before, but when it came to the ironwork he was entering into unknown territory. He was understandably cautious. Before any of the ironwork reached the site, the 9-foot-long links were rigorously tested to a 100-per-cent safety margin, heated and dipped into oil to prevent corrosion, then dried off in stoves. The links were then accurately bored on a jig. But that still left important questions undecided. No one could be quite sure what strains would be involved when the chains were constructed, loaded and stretched to the correct curvature. Sections of chain were carted off to a nearby valley where a remarkably Heath Robinson experimental rig was set up. At the upper level, the chains were securely attached via pulleys to a solid support, and then fastened to a crank at the other end. This was held in shear legs and different loads were obtained by simply adding weights. It looks odd, but it was a perfectly sensible way of tackling what was really a brand-new problem.

The next issue that was raised was that of the vertical rods that would attach the curved chains to the horizontal deck. Now that, one would have thought, was a very basic calculation, but in the official account, Provis speaks with his master's voice: 'It is true that ordinates might have been determined by calculation, but with a practical man an experiment is always more simple and satisfactory than theoretical deductions.'[7] So a scale model was built to determine the rod lengths.

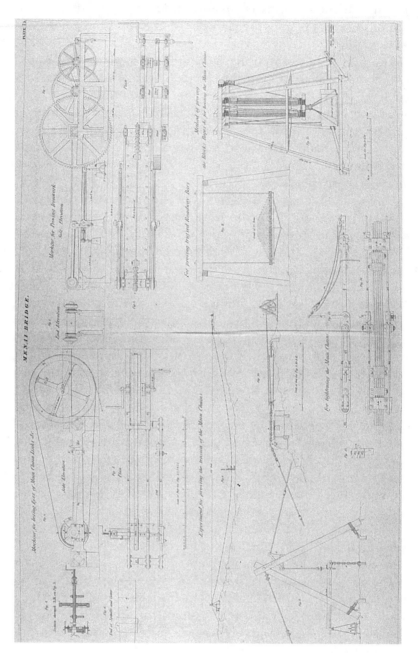

The complex system set up to test the chains for the Menai Bridge.

It is easy to forget when looking at the works for which Telford was responsible that he was a man who had begun as an apprentice mason and had never received any training in theory at all. He was not alone: even men such as the sophisticated John Rennie were inclined to take a dim view of 'book learning'. In such circumstances, the severely practical approach has an obvious appeal, and worked, but it still seems remarkable how little faith was placed in even the simplest mathematical calculations. But was it all pragmatic? The eminent politician and scientist Davies Gilbert wrote in his diary on 30 January 1826: 'By my recommendation the towers were raised and the curvature of the chains increased so as to nearly double the strength, the whole at the expense of 15 Thousand Pounds.' And the astronomer J. F. W. Herschel wrote to Gilbert in 1827: 'Passing the Menai Bridge (the sublimest of human works) I had occasion to applaud your suggestion of deepening the versed sine beyond Telford's original plan. It has an air of security that without the precaution would have been sorely deficient.'[8]

Telford soon realised that the original plan of simply securing the chains at the tops of the towers would lead to problems with forces tending to drag the towers inwards, so he arranged them to run on rollers. Other problems were not so easily solved. The chains were to be anchored by means of tunnels cut deep into the rock at the Anglesey end, but the tunnels kept filling with water. The simplest answer, in one sense, was to cut a drainage adit which would allow the water to run away. That was done, but it had to be carved out of the rock, and there was only space at the rock face for two men at a time. There were two shifts, and the four men took fourteen months, working day and night to hack out the adit. It was a laborious business, but necessary to avoid long-term problems with corrosion, and is typical of Telford's thoroughness. His ability to consider every detail in his planning was never seen to better effect than on the great day on when the first chain was set in place on 26 April 1825.

The chain was assembled in two sections and suspended over the towers. A raft was built, 400 feet long by 6 feet wide (122 by 2 metres), held together by iron bars, on which the two ends of the chains were to be connected, and platforms built out from the banks to help manoeuvre everything into position. The chains were attached at the shore side to pulley systems worked by capstans turned by a force of 150 labourers. As it was absolutely necessary that everything was co-ordinated, fife bands played to keep the men in time.

At first the men had little to do but haul up the slack of the tackles, but when those were tightened, and the weight of the chain which was gradually rising began to be felt, the race Which they had hitherto run at the capstan was reduced to a steady trot.

As work went on, the drifting tide caught the raft and it swung away with the water, and for the first time it was possible to see that the chains were joined and suspended. In an hour and a half from the start of operations it was all over.

Mr Telford now ascended the pyramid to satisfy himself that all was right; and there, surrounded by his assistants, the contractors, and as many as could find a place to stand on received the congratulations of many a friend to the bridge. The hats on the pyramid were soon off, the signal was understood by all around, and three cheers loud and long closed the labours of the day.

It was a day of triumph in which the men shared, two of the more daring amongst them celebrating the event by walking right over the chains from one bank to the other.

It was a propitious beginning, but as work proceeded and more chains were added and the road deck connected, it began to appear that no one had made sufficient allowance for the wind effect. This was something that did not show up with models, but was certainly felt by the men on the site.[9]

When the chains were hanging singly (with a gale of wind) the vibration was from 6 to 8 inches each way, & probably a little more at times: and if the wind struck the chain obliquely the undulation was considerable but I never could ascertain to what extent correctly – When we began to connect the chain with the short suspenders both these motions were reduced. When the roadway was begun suspending on both sides (it was blowing a gale nearly the whole time) the undulation and vibration was very great. The men had great difficulty in standing without holding on at times. The motion resembled much a ship riding at anchor when blowing fresh – as we advanced towards the centre the motion diminished very much. We are now screwing the first tier of plank down to the roadway bars & at every strake that is fastened I perceive it gets stiffer so when the three tier is all secured with skirting boards, side railings etc the vibration & undulation I conceive will scarcely be perceptible.

There were more alarms over the next few months, but in spite of these early troubles, the bridge was opened at midnight on 30 January 1826.

There was a quiet crossing with the mail coach early in the morning, seen by few apart from those who were most intimately concerned, including Hazeldine – but not Telford. The previous few weeks, when the bridge seemed to want to twist itself inside out, had been an immense strain, and he was not ready to announce any great public ceremonies. Seeing it opened was the thing, and he went across himself, later in the day, satisfied at last that all was well.

All was not quite well, however. Reports came in of the platform being twisted in severe gales, which caused fractures in some of the vertical rods. Extra strengthening was applied and seemed to have solved the problem. Then a serious accident occurred in which it was alleged that the bridge had moved so far that the mail coach had toppled over, bringing down the horses which had to be cut free of their harness. A closer investigation revealed that the coachman was blind drunk! Telford's masterpiece still stands.

In all the excitement, the other major bridge along the route seems almost insignificant. In any other circumstances, the Conwy bridge would have been a marvel, and was undeniably a great boon. Once again, a dangerous ferry crossing was replaced by a safe, smooth ride on a well-maintained roadway. There were no dramas during construction, and even the setting of the chains in place seemed a routine matter after Menai. Telford did not even turn up in person, and heard the news by letter.[10]

> Have the pleasure to inform you that the first chain was taken over at Conway Bridge yesterday ... 12 6½ inch ropes ... was stretched across from the towers one each side, and cross planks was laid on these at about 10 feet apart, four breadths of planks were laid lengthway on these which formed a complete gangway. When this was brought to the desired curve, we commenced building the chain which was accomplished in a short time & everything safe, the ropes stretched considerably and caused a greater deflection than wanted, but this can easily be adjusted by screws.

By the time the opening day arrived, however, there was no longer any doubt that the suspension bridge was strong and secure and there were great celebrations. First came the Chester Mail crowded 'with as many passengers as could possibly find a place about it that they could hold by. The horses went steadily over, which was more than I expected they would, as the people were shouting and screaming by the side of them from the embankment to the pier, the passengers at the same time singing God Save the King as loud as they could.'[11]

As the day progressed more and more people appeared.

At one time the Bridge was so crowded that it was difficult to move along. Most of the carriages of the neighbouring gentry, Stage Coaches, Post Chaises, gigs & horse passed repeatedly over, and kept up a continuous procession for several hours ... everyone appeared satisfied with the safety of the bridge and delighted that they could go home and say 'I crossed the first day it was opened'.

At Conwy, Telford had the perfect excuse to indulge the sense of romanticism he had shown in Scotland, and added castellations to the towers to echo the even grander fortifications of the castle that rose above the bridge. And he even discarded his standard toll-house designs in favour of his very own miniature castle, bristling with towers and ramparts. What is not so immediately apparent is that the bridge represents only the smaller part of the water crossing, and that the main section consists of an embankment, 2015 feet (614 metres) long, 300 feet (91.5 metres) wide at the base and 30 feet (9 metres) at the top. The base was two parallel stone ridges built out from the shore, then packed with mountain clay, which had to be immediately faced with stone to stop it being washed away at the next high tide. At first, material had to be brought by boat, but as the bank advanced, carts travelled over the top. If the embankment tends to be ignored, so too does the other important structure on the Holyhead Road.

The old road took a very indirect route on the final stage of the journey to Holyhead, taking a loop round the end of the broad shallow bay to cross the narrows at Four Mile Bridge. Telford decided to take a direct line across the sands of Beddmanarch Bay by means of an embankment. One reason why it can be so easily overlooked is its iceberg-like quality. The top is the standard road width, but the base spreads at the bottom to 114 feet (34.7 metres). It runs for nearly a mile and, like so many of Telford's works along this route, remains in use.

The success of the road was matched by the success of the harbour at Holyhead. In his 1824 report, Telford indicated that success was bringing its own problems.

I have more than once seen about 100 [ships] in at a time, but this crowding within the protection of the pier is a serious interruption to the Steam Packets, and for a want of a sufficient room two trading vessels of large Burthen, having failed in obtaining a berth, were driven to, and wrecked on the opposite or Eastern shore.

Sir John Stanley, whose name survives in the Stanley Embankment, was the chairman of the harbour commissioners and supported Telford's

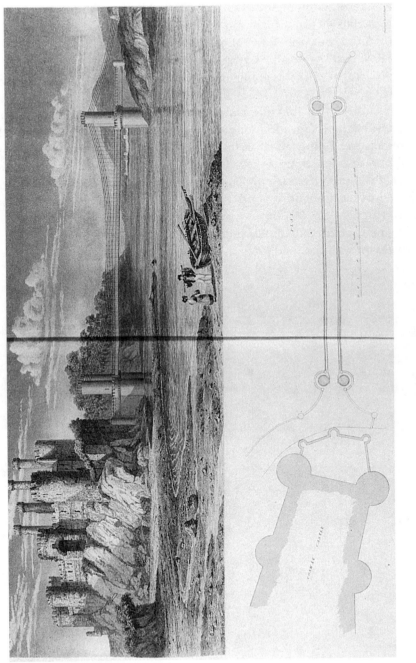

Conwy Bridge.

view that something had to be done. With an annual tonnage now running at 100,000 tons, the harbour was both too constricted and too shallow.[12] As a result, £4000 was allocated for deepening the inner harbour to allow small vessels to lay up out of the way of the packets. Similar improvement work was going on at Howth on the other side of the Irish Sea.

It is no wonder that one looks back on such times as part of a heroic age of engineering, when one man could not only control such works spread over hundreds of miles, but could devise structures that were bigger than anything ever attempted before and wholly innovative. What is more, this was only one part of a whole range of projects. And one further thought to ponder: had Telford been working under modern rules and regulations, he would have attended the bridge opening as a pensioner enjoying his retirement, not as an active man in a hurry to get on with the next job.

CHAPTER THIRTEEN

Pro Bono Publico

If the book had stopped here, readers would have had an impression of a great engineer responsible for great works, which would have been a perfectly valid picture. The last chapter left Telford in his late sixties, enjoying the successful completion of his most important project, and it would not have been in the least unreasonable if he had declared enough was enough and reached for the carpet slippers. But what is missing from the picture is any account of the less than four-star attractions with which he was concerned at the same time, either briefly or as the principal engineer. This chapter will deal with some of these – and then the fact that if he ever bought slippers, they probably stayed in the box, will seem all the more remarkable. Much of the work came through the Exchequer Loan Office, usually beginning with a simple note explaining that some group had requested a loan for public works and asking Telford to look at the details and report back. Sometimes the matter ended there, with the loan refused; at other times he must have heartily wished that he had turned in a negative report in the first place and saved himself a mass of trouble. Nowhere was this more true than on the Gloucester & Berkeley, later the Gloucester & Sharpness, Canal.

Work had begun in 1793, but by 1802, everything had ground to a halt, and even visits by such experienced engineers as Jessop and Thomas Dadford did little to improve matters, and only increased the wrath of one shareholder, who had himself been chief engineer when work began, Robert Mylne. One has to allow for a certain professional jealousy here.[1]

Well, my Good Sir,

   I had your 2 Summonses to attend general meetings of 29 Sept. & 12
Oct[r]. – Is there nothing going forward with the Canal? Is it to lay
Dorment in a deserted State for ever? – It always was in want of a
Chancellor of the Exchequer, & a better Chairman – Till this time, I have
not had leisure to reflect on the miserable and misguided State of it, and
its lamentable fate – It is a work that requires other talent & knowledge
than a common Canal Cutter – From the time of *Jessop's* visit, I date its
misfortunes. He and Dadford are mere drudges in that confined school;
and both are without any sense of extended honour. The G. Junction is
in a Dreadfull State, & required to have its difficult points all recon-
structed. I have lately surveyed it. The Irish are advertising for a Resident
Engineer. I think Dadford and they would fit one another to a T, for
wrong heads and deficiency of knowledge.

Early problems seem to have stemmed from using small contractors
for a difficult project – one can scarcely believe that anyone was
capable of constructing a ship canal who had to borrow planks from
the company before he could start work, but that was the case in 1795.
Worse still was the general incompetence of the committee, which
explains why such contracts were handed out in the first place.
Matters were still languishing nearly twenty years later, when Telford
was called in.[2] He was asked to report on the 'practical [sic] and
utility' of finishing the canal and estimate the likely revenue. He was
also to report, rather alarmingly given the fierce currents and
immense tidal rise and fall of the Severn, on whether vessels could
reach Sharpness, the southern terminus, including 'those who are
accustomed to drift with the tides'. The initial job of fact finding went
to John Upton, who was soon also reporting on other schemes for
Telford. But although Telford necessarily had to delegate a great deal
of work to assistants, he still went to make his own final assessment,
and it seems he was not unduly worried about the conditions during
his visit, for Upton sent a worried note hoping that he 'did not take a
cold from walking so much on our spoil banks'. It was a brief survey,
at the end of which he recommended that work should go ahead, but
with the proviso that there had to be enough cash available to see the
whole thing through: 'Anything short of this would be delusion and
disgrace.'[3]

Work did go ahead, but in an atmosphere which was scarcely
conducive to good management. The resident engineer, John
Woodhouse, was to have a brief career once Telford's eye was turned
on him. He was discovered to have been ordering building materials,

wearing his engineering hat, and paying too high a price for inferior stone – which might have been just about excusable if he had not been buying the stone from his own son.[4]

Woodhouse went; in his place came a new and better man, Thomas Fletcher, and Telford was quick to impose his own strict system. It was, he wrote, underlined for emphasis, 'absolutely necessary' to have a resident engineer who had no direct financial interest in either contracts or supply of material. It is not hard to sympathise with the engineers working for inefficient companies who all too often found themselves working very hard in difficult situations, performing their side of the bargain, but not even receiving the pay to which they were entitled. Upton had the misfortune not only to be working for the inept Gloucester management, but also on another of Telford's problem projects, the Thames & Medway Canal, which was to prove if anything rather worse. Telford offered sympathy but not much else.[5]

> I had a letter from the Clerk of the Thames and Medway Canal Company yesterday telling me that he had received directions to pay me your account of £40 2 0 and expected to be in town in a few days and could call upon me – this, however, is not the first promise I have received to the same effect, and therefore I shall not give credit to the sincerity of it, till I touch the cash. Being on this subject, it occurs to me to submit to you to the propriety of you transmitting your further accounts, viz. Gloster and B Canal, Folkestone Harbour, Shoreham Harbour, and any others, if any you have ... I will collect them for you, and pay the amount as you shall direct.

Poor Upton was soon to have more problems to face; he seems to have fallen out with Fletcher, and perhaps he had rather too high an opinion of his own capabilities. Whatever the reason, his career on the canal came to an end, and the unhappy man was reduced to making desperate pleas.[6]

> You was as good as, to make in your note (when here) some very handsome allusions as to my talent, and I wish I could convince you that I do not require such salary as you may imagine and that I would be very grateful to assist in any thing; if it only produced two pounds per week; and in fact rather than idle, I will be glad to be employed *where you are concerned*, for nothing until you find an opportunity of placing me.

Meanwhile, the canal remained a shambles and Fletcher was soon joining the chorus of complaints raised by the unpaid. It took time for Telford to get everything moving in the way he wanted. A big step forward came in 1823, when Hugh McIntosh, described as a 'Contractor for Public Works' from Bermondsey, undertook to complete the whole canal in two years for an agreed price of £111,493 15s. 11d., which was actually more than Mylne's estimated cost for the entire project when work began.[7]

McIntosh was one of the biggest contractors of the day, with adequate finance to provide the men and equipment to do the job. By 1825, there were up to five hundred men on site, with over a hundred horses, and work was going on apace – at too great a pace, according to Fletcher. That year, an estimated 2000 cubic yards (1500 cubic metres) of sea wall was washed away by a high tide at Sharpness, because, it was suggested, the work had been rushed. Anyone reading accounts of canal building will find this a constant refrain. The advantages of using an important contractor were obvious, but there could be problems as well. With a fixed-price contract, such as McIntosh's, the quicker it was done, the less he had to pay in wages and the higher the profit. If the resident engineer let him set the pace then there was always the chance of the sort of catastrophe that happened at Sharpness, but if he was meticulous in maintaining standards, the contractor might well prefer to shift his resources to one of his other sites, where the engineer was less fussy. Fletcher, having complained about excess speed, was soon facing the second problem, and was constantly asking Telford to put pressure on McIntosh. Telford, of course, had other preoccupations, and he was actually considering a proposal for extending the ship canal up-river to Worcester, where it would meet the new Worcester & Birmingham Canal. That scheme came to nothing, but Fletcher became ever more desperate to have Telford on site: 'The period is just approaching, and not very distant, when we must, as matter of necessity request the favour of you to devote a day, or Two, to the perambulation of the whole line.'[8]

The following year, the canal was opened and it somehow sums up the history of a 17-mile-long canal that had taken over thirty years to build that the ceremony should end in farce. When the lock was finally opened at Sharpness to unite canal and river, three local lads decided that the official junketing needed livening up. They found an ancient cannon, stuffed it with wadding and applied the light, at which point the whole thing exploded. But to set against that is the fact that the canal was a great success. Gloucester developed into an important inland port, and Sharpness was greatly improved and developed over the years. Traffic flowed from the start, more than doubling in the first four full years of operation. It may have been a confounded nuisance to Telford, but in commercial terms it was a great deal more successful than his other highly praised ship canal in Scotland. Traffic on the canal itself has dwindled, but ships were still calling in at Sharpness at the end of the twentieth century.

Two other ship canals reached at least the start of the planning stage. The first, the Liverpool Ship Canal, was intended to cross the Wirral peninsula, but Telford was quick to detect an odour of corruption rising from that project and hastily backed away. The second was a project that cropped up from time to time throughout the canal age, for a ship canal to link the English and Bristol Channels, so that coasting vessels could avoid the dangers of Lands End and the Cornish coast. Rennie had looked at the idea in 1811, and Telford followed on. He devised a route that started near Bridgwater on the north coast and ended at Beer, a tiny fishing village just outside Seaton. Vessels were to be limited to 150 tons, but even so there were formidable engineering works involved, with sixty locks in 44½ miles: the mind boggles at what the rate of progress would have been. New ports were also to be constructed, and the cost of whole works was estimated at £1,750,000. Amazingly, investors were found to promise most of the money on the basis of estimated profits.[9]

> In addition to the great advantage which must necessarily accrue to the shipping interest, the prospects held out to the speculator in this work, are sufficient to tempt the cupidity of the most sceptical, if reliance may be placed in the accuracy of the data from whence the proprietors have derived the probable sources of revenue. In a prospectus, published by the committee on this navigation, it is stated, that the clear annual income applicable to a dividend among the proprietors, is calculated, by very low estimates, to amount to twelve per cent. or £210,846, 12s. 4d.

The writer did, however, add that 'the reader must bear in mind that the latter end of 1824 was a time of high expectations'. So it was, and the Bill was duly passed by Parliament, just as those high expectations gave way to a general feeling of financial gloom and despair. The promised money never came, and by 1828, the committee had to admit defeat, which is probably just as well. It would never have been another Gloucester & Sharpness.

One canal that was completed would have been better had it enjoyed the fate of the English and Bristol Channel Canal. This was the Ulster Canal, part of a grand scheme to link Belfast and Newry to the country's most important navigable river, the Shannon. The Ulster Canal was to leave the River Blackwater, that runs into the southern end of Lough Neagh, to join the River Finn at Upper Lough Earne. It was not a project that greatly appealed to Telford – his early enthusiasm for Ireland had long since evaporated. On an earlier visit to Dublin, the best that he was able to say about the 'Land of Shamrocks' was that 'it enables me to set a higher value upon our own'.[10] He was required to make two trips in order to see the project started. Of the first in 1826, he simply noted that, as with many Irish questions at that time, there was no shortage of differing opinions: 'I made an extensive and rapid excursion in Ireland amidst extreme heat in every sense of the word.'[11] His report appeared and nothing happened. Then the whole scheme was revived in 1828, and he had to survey the whole route again; this time the loan commissioners put up £125,000. Work was destined to drag along to an opening in 1841, and in the end the canal proved of almost no value as it was made too small to take the vessels in use on its connecting waterways. Even in the 1990s, when it seemed almost any canal could be considered a candidate for restoration, a proposal to spend a startling £80 million on the Ulster was soundly rejected. It definitely does not count among Telford's successes.

It would be tedious to list every canal on which Telford was required to give a view by the loan commissioners. Some, such as the Union Canal in Scotland, proved very successful, and it was carried through under its chief engineer, Hugh Baird, with Hugh McIntosh once again taking the lion's share of the contracting work. Telford's credit extends no further than having given his approval to a reasonable plan. Others were less successful, verging on disastrous. The Portsmouth & Arundel Canal, between the River Arun and Chichester Harbour, was perfectly satisfactory as a navigation, but no one had allowed for the fact that it would permit sea water to come inland, seep under the gravel and pollute the water supply of Portsmouth. As a result, the huge compensation that the canal company had to pay totally ruined them. Telford was no more to be blamed for this than he was to be praised for the success of the Union.

Just as he was involved with other canals during this period, so too was he busy advising on roads. He was always very open and honest in his reports. He was asked, for example, to report on the road between Shaftesbury and Honiton. He found it 'so hilly, crooked. and in many places narrow that it is quite incompatible with the present rapid mode of travel'.[12] He did, however, add a very important rider. 'It is however proper to render the Trustees distinctly aware that improvements can only be accomplished at a very heavy expence ... and perhaps you may consider it advisable to comunicate this hasty sketch, and consult them, before further expence is occurred.' They were consulted, they agreed to a full survey and the cost was, as predicted, high. It does, however, help to explain why everyone seemed prepared to trust Telford.

His surveying teams were spread far and wide throughout the 1820s, but two main routes took up a great deal of their time. The first was the Great North Road from London to Edinburgh. This is a route of great antiquity, but that does not mean that the alignment has remained unchanged. The oldest route follows the line of Roman Ermine Street, and the medieval route offered a number of local alternatives – becoming, in effect, the Great North Roads. In time, one route came to predominate, though it was not necessarily the best line. Telford proposed a major realignment. Where the old way wobbles well away from a straight line drawn between the two cities, particularly at the northern end where it follows the coast, he wanted to take a very direct route, with 'a mail coach road of the most perfect construction'. This would offer better alignments, less severe gradients and reduce the overall distance by around 30 miles. As he recognised, this could never be done with private trusts, but would have to depend on the parliamentary commissioners. In the event, all he was able to achieve was an improvement on a few miles of road south of Edinburgh.

The next important scheme was for the alternative route to Ireland, via the new steam-packet service from Milford Haven to Waterford. Telford was asked to look at two alternatives for the route as far as Carmarthen.[13] The first was to go through Bristol with a ferry crossing of the Severn, the second, west from Northleach via Gloucester and Brecon. The one proviso was that any road should include as many 'post towns' as possible. The main problem on the Bristol route was the Severn crossing, where the estuary has the second largest tidal rise and fall of anywhere in the world, and the obvious crossing places revealed alarming rocks and sand banks at low tide, and whirling currents at high tide. Telford himself described it as 'one of the most forbidding' ferry crossings he had ever come across. He was all for making a brand-new ferry nearer the mouth near what is now Weston-super-Mare. In the event, two crossings were to be regularly used, the Old Passage, replaced this century by the splendid Severn Bridge, and the New Passage, by what is now the second Severn crossing. The alternative route proved to be a touch controversial. There was a great clamour from Cheltenham for a road, as the rapidly developing spa was 'very much resorted to by numbers of Irish families of the first respectability'. The town, in fact, still retains its Irish connection, though whether all the visitors who flood in for Gold Cup week can fairly be described as of the first respectability is a different matter. The Cheltenham contingent were not content to wait for Telford, but promoted their very own route, and their own river crossing above Gloucester at The Haw. They were premature. Their route was not favoured, and all that the bridge now carries is a B-road serving a number of small villages. Telford opted for the obvious route through Gloucester.

Two experienced men were given the work of surveying the route, Joseph Mitchell and Henry Welch, and the latter's surviving letters to Telford give a vivid picture of the problems that faced the men on the ground. Welch set off from Northleach, where he seemed rather upset when local farmers indicated that they would rather he and his men did not stomp through their corn fields just as they were about to harvest them. He came back later, but had more problems just north of the Forest of Dean, *en route* to Ross-on-Wye.[14]

> One field of wheat, however, remained only partially cut when I reached it. My men were obliged to leave the field otherwise they would have been ill treated by the reapers who were mostly intoxicated and Lawless Fellows from the Forest. An instance of their effrontery was some of them lifted my Portmanteau containing the letters you sent me and threw it into a Field of Barley where it remained, supposed to have been stolen, until the Barley was cut.

In the end, the report was produced in June 1825, but once again no action was taken. At least there were other bodies prepared to find actual work. Telford was able to return to an old friend, as it were, in his bridge-building career as he once again planned crossings of the River Severn in the 1820s. By now, he and Hazledine knew exactly what they were doing and at two of the crossings, Holt Fleet, north of Worcester, and Mythe Bridge, near Tewkesbury, they produced two classic arches of cast iron. Mythe Bridge has particularly attractive detailing. The masonry abutments are pierced by Gothic arches for flood relief, and the same device is repeated for purely decorative effect in the piers. Telford would have liked to have done something similar at Over on the outskirts of Gloucester, but the civic authorities felt that cast iron was beneath their dignity and demanded something grander in stone.

It must have been rather tiresome for Telford, who had, in effect, ready-made plans for Severn bridges which he was not permitted to use.

So, if he could not do it the easy way, why not try something quite different? Jean Perronet, who was head of the Ponts et Chaussées in the years leading up to the French Revolution, was doing in stone what Telford had been doing in iron, building flatter arches, with narrow arch rings and more delicate piers. Telford liked the feeling of lightness he had achieved in his two iron bridges, and tried out Perronet's ideas at Gloucester. His model was the bridge over the Seine at Neuilly, but with his own variations. The most striking feature is the arch itself, the shape based on two ellipses with the same chord length but a considerable difference in the rise. It is difficult to explain the concept in words, but looking under the main arch the effect is rather like the nipped-in waist of an Edwardian lady. He was very well pleased with the result.

He was less pleased with what happened during the construction. He had used good stone, taking it from the same quarry at Ardley that he had used for Bewdley Bridge, but he had not taken enough care in laying the foundations. As the centring was eased, it soon became clear that the arch was dropping. It was a peculiarity of the Perronet method that the centring had to come down in a piece, so there was no chance of any remedial work once it was decided to remove it. The arch fell an alarming 10 inches. Telford was mortified, but took the blame onto himself 'for having suffered an ill-judged parsimony to prevail in the foundations of the wing-walls, leaving them unsupported by piles and platforms'.[15] He was quite convinced that if he had done what needed to be done there would have been a drop of no more than 3 inches. But it has to be said that the bridge is still in place, if a little forlorn, overshadowed by its modern replacement carrying the A40 dual carriageway.

During this same period, he was able to return to another area of expertise which he acquired through his work in Scotland: harbour construction. He became involved in a minor way in improving the harbour at Dublin's port of Howth. But now he was to become a leading figure in an altogether grander scheme located in the very heart of the capital, literally in the shadow of the Tower of London. This was for a new enclosed dock, opening off the Pool of London. The work was divided into two parts: Telford was to be responsible for designing the actual dock, with its entrance locks and harbour. The design of the surrounding warehouses went to Philip Hardwick, who was to do even grander things in the railway age, including the once noble great hall at Euston and the splendid triumphant arch that formed the entrance to the station – both of which have fallen victim to mindless official vandalism. At least his work at the new dock was not to suffer a similar fate.

Not everyone was in favour of a new dock so near the heart of London, especially the various companies who had spent a great deal of money on developing the London Dock complex further downstream. One of the attractions was new legislation, the Warehouse Act of 1823, which allowed goods to be stored duty free in bonded warehouses. There was also a great deal to be said for having a wholly enclosed dock with secure warehousing instead of open wharves which were an open invitation to thieves and pilferers, while saving cash on duty was a real bonus. Approval was given to the scheme by Parliament, and the Act allowed for compulsory purchase of land, even though there were people living in over a thousand homes on the site. The new dock took its name from the hospital which also originally stood there, becoming St Katharine's Dock.

It presented both Telford and Hardwick with some difficult problems. The site was an awkward shape and very constricted. Hardwick did his part in saving space by conceiving an ingenious system of building his warehouses out over the wharf area, supporting the upper storeys by cast-iron pillars set at the quayside. More space was saved by having recesses in the façade to take simple cranes. It still left Telford with a problem, but one he was able to turn to advantage.[16]

> When the space necessary for warehouses and entrances was subtracted 10 acres only remained for the actual docks. – It being obvious that the accommodation required could not be obtained by the simple forms of squares and parallelograms, I was, from necessity, led to adapt the shape of the docks to that of the ground: and this was so managed, after attentive consideration, as to become really advantageous, as affording an increased extent of wharfage and two docks instead of one, by which distribution of trade was likely to be better arranged; with a further advantage, that in case it should at any time be found necessary to empty one dock, the water may be retained at full height in the other.

This was an immense scheme, and Telford's estimate of £242,000 for engineering works looks quite modest when set against the £1,353,000 needed to purchase land and property. The main contract for the engineering works went to George Burge for £190,000, while Telford had his man on the spot as 'inspecting foreman', the ever reliable Thomas Rhodes, who had proved his worth at Menai. Everything about this scheme was on a gargantuan scale. Once the site had been cleared, a coffer dam had to be built to allow excavation below river level. Piling engines were brought in, able to drive one pile a day, but these piles were 1 foot square, 44 feet (13.4 metres) long and had to be driven down through 10 feet of stiff clay. Soon work was proceeding at a ferocious rate. The first stone for the dock walls was laid on 3 May 1827. The scene of great activity was described by a Swedish visitor, Captain Carlsund. He saw a thousand men at work, railways laid with horse-drawn waggons to carry the spoil, a pumping engine, barrow runs and a temporary jetty for loading earth into waiting barges.[17] There was one moment of near disaster, when an exceptionally high tide breached the bank and flooded the entire site. Happily, no workers were injured.

There were new problems to be faced all the time, particularly with water supply to fill the entrance lock and to top up the basins. The great advantage of Telford's long career was that he never had any doubt where to turn when such difficulties arose. He went almost automatically to Boulton and Watt, and it was James Watt junior who came down to London to solve the problem. He installed one 80-horse-power engine to pump water from the river to fill the entrance lock, which was supplied at the same time in a more conventional way by sluices from the basin. A second engine was used to refill the basin while ships were passing through. As a result, the 180-foot (55-metre) lock could be filled in just over five minutes.

Incredibly, the first ship entered the dock on 25 October 1828, just over three years after the Act was approved. In that time, plans and specifications had been prepared and approved, tenders submitted and accepted, property purchased, the site cleared and the dock built. It was all rather too much for Telford. 'As a practical engineer, responsible for the success of difficult operations, I must be allowed to protest against such haste, pregnant as it was, and ever will be, with risks, which in more instances than one severely tested all my experience and skill, involving dangerously the reputation of the directors and their engineer.'[18] Telford may have worried, but the work was well done and stood the tests of use and time.

Not content with such a load of more or less familiar work, Telford was also quite ready to take up new challenges. He was about to follow his mentor, William Jessop, into the difficult world of fen drainage – difficult not so much for the engineering works as for the political infighting. He was, in fact, about to enter waters far murkier than the dirtiest fenland ditch. The story began back in the 1780s, when the mainland to the west of King's Lynn was drained by an artificial cut that led

into the River Ouse, which at that point was passing through an extravagant bend. Various engineers were brought in, whose names are
already familiar: Jessop himself, Robert Mylne, John Golborne and
John Rennie. An obvious improvement was a straight channel across
the bend of roughly three miles which would ease the flow of water and
improve navigation at the same time. It was to be called the Eau Brink,
and Parliament argued about it for three years from 1793 to 1795, one
year for each mile of cut. The Act was finally passed, but still nothing
happened as the factions continued to argue. Eventually, the whole
matter went to arbitration, with Rennie appearing for the drainage
interests, Telford speaking for the navigation, with a Captain Huddart
given the job of umpire to keep order between the two engineers and
a variety of local interests. At last, in 1818, Huddart approved a very
modest cut and Rennie and Telford collaborated in the work. It was to
be one of Rennie's last projects, for he died in 1821. It was, predictably,
not a huge success. The cut proved an inadequate drain and Telford
had to return with Rennie's son – who was to become the very eminent
Sir John Rennie – and do the work all over again to provide a wider,
deeper channel. This time, the results were entirely satisfactory.

In spite of these tribulations, Telford worked on in the Fens, complaining all the time about the back-biting and petty jealousies that
seemed to afflict almost everyone from local landowners to the official
commissioners and administrators. He supported a plan for improving
the Nene, but as some felt it would cut the town of Wisbech off from
the river, the inhabitants of what was after all a thriving small port
objected. It seems to have been the last straw for Telford, who fulmi-
nated against them in his autobiography.[19]

> At what time and in what manner the River Nene will be improved up
> to and past the town of Wisbech, and from thence to Peterborough, is
> very uncertain, as the inhabitants of Wisbech still inherit a full portion
> of the perverse disposition which Mr. Wells, in his History of the Fens
> records, as heretofore forcibly obstructing the formation of Kinderley's
> Cut. This instance, and the violent opposition to my plan in 1821 for a
> new river-course and floating dock, a measure calculated to improve
> and establish their port as equal or superior to Lynn, may serve to char-
> acterise a people, not only indisposed to promote the general
> improvement of the adjacent country, but totally incapable of judging
> of what would have been manifestly beneficial to themselves.

This, it has to be remembered, was written some time after the event,
and Telford had no fond memories of that low, brooding landscape. It

was while returning from a survey in the company of John Gibb and the younger Rennie that he was caught in a downpour that soaked him to the skin. A few days later, something happened which was almost unheard of for that robust gentleman. He was taken seriously ill and had to stay in bed in Cambridge, instead of calling in on his various works. But if the Fens did badly by him, he did very well by them. One of the very last works for which he was engineer was the great North Level drain, a straight and navigable waterway that was to open in 1834.

Telford's years of incessant work and travel inevitably caught up with him in the end, and he began to feel that perhaps at the end of an arduous tour he would like something a little more personal and comfortable to come back to than rooms at a coffee house. He got himself a home.

CHAPTER FOURTEEN

London Days

For twenty-one years, Telford's only permanent home was in London, where he had rooms at the Salopian Coffee House. He became something of a famous fixture, holding court for friends, admirers and especially for young engineers. He was apparently considered such an asset that when he eventually announced he was to leave, the owner was horrified at the loss of his greatest asset, declaring that he had paid £75 for him to the previous owner! Even if it is not true, it is a good story, confirming the engineer's growing fame and importance. It also shows up a side of his character of which we only get the occasional glimpse in the surviving documents – his sociability – and you would have had to be very sociable indeed in 1821 to be worth £75 in coffee-house business. Telford, however, was not just a lure to bring in the customers; he was becoming quite a wealthy man. And we get some idea of just how wealthy from accounts of his investments in later life. Between 1825 and 1833 he salted away £26,000 in solidly secure 3 per cent annuities, as well as buying shares in projects in which he took an interest. To put that in perspective, you can balance that £26,000, bringing in £780 a year in interest, against the salary paid to Thomas Rhodes for overseeing the large and complex work involved in building St Katharine's Dock – £136 a year. Or to put it another way, it would have taken Rhodes four lifetimes to earn what Telford invested in eight years.

Telford was rich, but generous. His generosity became widely known, so that as a result he was pretty well besieged with requests for help – usually involving money.[1]

Numerous applications of this nature were incessantly made to him, and while in many cases the most liberal aid was afforded, I never knew an instance of unkind rejection. The profession of any talent, literary, scientific or mechanical, I always observed, was an irresistible passport to his bounty; although he seldom failed to accompany it with a rebuke, more or less gentle, yet conveyed in his own peculiarly effective manner, on the indiscretion and irregularities which too often led to the demand upon it.

The writer noted that he was particularly susceptible to pleas from fellow Scots, especially his old Eskdale connections. He was even prepared to help out those of whom he rather sternly disapproved. James Jackson, one of his distant relations, got himself into debt. This was just the sort of thing to bring down the Telfordian wrath, for he had no patience with weakness and incompetence. Jackson, he wrote, 'was always an obstinate, blundering fool'. His words were harsh, but not his actions. He paid for apprenticeships for the children, and sent £50 to William Little asking him to clear all Jackson's debts, and telling him to keep whatever was left over for his trouble in doing so.[2] Perhaps because he had no family of his own, he was always ready to help out the children of his old friends and colleagues. Matthew Davidson certainly knew just how useful the connection could be to his sons, Thomas and John, who were training to be surgeons, just as much as to James, who planned a career in engineering. He was constantly writing to them urging them to pay court to the great engineer and to ignore his eccentricities, which was a bit rich coming from Davidson.[3]

> I think you should not neglect to write to Mr. Telford letting him know what you have been doing lately at Nott^m. – what doing at London, and what you think of doing afterwards, asking his advice &c. if he do no notice you – never mind – keep writing away – there's nothing the matter, only, getting old and cross like your grey headed Dad.

That Telford did do a great deal for the family is borne out by a later letter in which Davidson reminds his son that 'you are bound by every tye of Gratitude to pay deference to his opinion'. There is also a hint that Telford might well have thought that the ratio of two doctors to one engineer was quite the wrong way round, for the letter ends: 'I threw the blame on you making John a Physician, as I find it answers best to let you fight it out with *The Old Gentleman* by yourselves.'[4]

He continued to help Thomas Campbell, the young poet of whom so much had been hoped. Campbell described Telford as a 'cicerone', who had introduced him into 'all descriptions of interesting society'. This comes as something of a surprise, since most others spoke of his rather limited social life. Perhaps it was his enthusiasm to promote the young man, who he clearly saw as a genius (see pp. 62–3) that made him put himself out for him. He must have been very gratified at finding his protégé achieving a great deal of success at the time and, more importantly, producing just the sort of verse of which he heartily approved. These were stirringly patriotic, including the well-known 'Mariners of England', destined to be bellowed out by hundreds of amateur choirs after it was set to music. He also provided the good Scot with a succession of equally heroic ballads.

> A chieftain to the Highlands bound
> Cries, 'Boatman, do not tarry!
> And I'll give thee a silver pound
> To row us o'er the ferry.'

Campbell remained a close friend and regular visitor and showed his appreciation of the help he had received by naming his first son Thomas Telford Campbell. His friend's success was a source of immense pride to Telford, but his greatest practical help was offered to young trainee engineers, who were made particularly welcome if they happened to be related to old colleagues. He was eventually able to do a great deal towards putting his young men on the way to a first-rate career.

At the age of sixty-four, Telford had spent much of his life travelling the country, sometimes staying in decent hotels, but often having to make do with the best some remote corner of the Highlands could offer. And at the end of his travels he came back to his rented rooms at the coffee shop. Now, he finally decided he wanted a home of his own and bought 24 Abingdon Street in Westminster. It was a large house, as befitted a wealthy and distinguished gentleman, but he had no intention of keeping it all to himself. Rooms were set aside for the young engineers who came to him as pupils and assistants. One of these was Joseph Mitchell, whose father had worked on the Highland roads and in whose footsteps he was eventually to follow (see p. 105). If one reads what Telford wrote about the need for stern dedication and unstinting hard work he can seem almost tyrannical. He certainly believed in learning by practice, as he himself had done, and left his protégés in no doubt that there was no easy route to their chosen career. In a letter he wrote to a Miss Malcolm, who had tried to persuade Telford to help a young would-be engineer, he offered a grim life in the short term with only grimmer prospects to follow.[5]

I am this morning favoured with yours of the 5th and regret that I shall not be able to be of much service in regard to the young man you take an interest in, and who appears so deserving of encouragement; above half a century of increasing Exertions, warn me to contract my engagements; this I am now doing by declining new undertakings, and those now in hand, are fully occupied by deserving, experienced persons who have volunteered their Services; in fact, the profession has more candidates than can be employed; the *Lottery is great*, the *valuable Tickets* few so that when my opinion is required I uniformly advise to consider whether Architecture or Land Surveying are not more certain pursuits, they are more readily acquired, and more generally in demand.

If civil Engineering is, after all, still preferred, the way in which both the late M[r] Rennie and myself proceeded, was to serve a regular apprenticeship to some practical employment, he to a Millwright and I to a general Housebuilder, in this way we secured the means, by hard labour, of earning subsistence and in time by degrees, acquiring the confidence of our employers and the public, rose into what is denominated Civil Engineering –

This is the true way of acquiring practical Skill, a thorough knowledge of Materials to be employed, and altho' last, not least, a perfect knowledge of the habits and disposition of Workmen.

What ambitious young man would welcome such advice or choose to work for such a man? But those who did found reality very different, as Mitchell described.[6]

Our working hours were from nine till seven; the evenings we could dispose of as we liked. The old gentleman treated us as sons. If he had friends we dined in their company. His house was handsome, quite suited for his requirements, and in accordance with his professional position, and he was very proud of it. After having lived in lodgings and hotels all his life, he appeared gratified and delighted at the additional comfort and convenience of his new residence. When any new friend called and complimented him on his new quarters he used to say 'Oh, you must see my house,' taking them over the principal apartments, pointing out the solid mahogany doors and marble chimney pieces. 'Below,' he would say, 'I have a perfect village'; and opening the door of the apartment in which we worked, he added 'and here are two raw Scotchmen.' He usually finished up by observing 'It is a singular coincidence that I, a bridge builder, should occupy the house of the engineer of Westminster Bridge, Labelye; and there, in a panel above the chimney-piece in the dining-room, is a picture of the bridge by Canaletto.'

Some years before, William Little had written to Telford asking if he could help his son James in his career, and Telford had replied asking for samples of the schoolboy's work. He was sufficiently impressed to offer encouragement, and when the young man appeared in London at the start of a business career he was rapidly absorbed into the Abingdon Street household. Now, all notions of the elderly engineer as some dour, grumbling Scotsman are blown away.[7]

> In the beginning of November he sent me a note saying that he wished if my business would permit, that I would come to Abingdon Street. My business permitted, and my inclination favoured it, so I went ... We breakfast at 8 and dine at ½ past 5 – this would not suit you, but now that I am accustomed to it, I like it very well. Mr. T. is very fond of the mutton ham which is only presented on great occasions, & Mr. Anderson & I get a little now and then by way of a treat – we have large dinner parties sometimes, & a fine *set out* there is – but do not you imagine that Mr. T. eats nothing but cake & drinks nothing but water, if you do, you are quite mistaken, we drink wine *every day,* you will think I dare say that this is very like '*extravagance*'! ... a day seldom passes without his telling stories.

The only note of sternness is revealed in a footnote, remarking that anyone arriving late for breakfast went hungry. In reminiscing about Telford in later life, Little remembered many times sitting with the engineer talking over the old days in Eskdale. This high-spirited young man stayed with Telford for three years before joining the staff of the Governor of Bombay. Even afterwards, the two kept up a regular correspondence. Telford wanted to know everything there was to know about India, and obviously found the picture of life out there to be of quite an exotic, not to say luxurious, kind. He noted wryly that his own servant 'thinks that your servants must be poor creatures and their numbers cumbersome'. But Telford himself had the true imperial spirit. He was quite sure India was a country 'where comfort and happiness, must be greater under the mild British Government, than when harrassed by the contentions of their remorseless Chiefs'.[8]

Telford was not even greatly put out by a letter from Little describing the funerary rites of the Parsees of Bombay, who exposed corpses on open towers, where they provided food for the vultures, and thus contributed in their way to the life cycles of eternity. Very interesting, no doubt, but not perhaps the most tactful topic to raise with a seventy-five year old not enjoying particularly good health. But the only response was a sardonic 'the vulture is certainly an uncouth Angelic Judge' and the perhaps surprising conclusion in that age, that it really made no difference how the body was disposed of as long as 'respect is preserved'.[9] Thomas Telford was certainly neither conventional nor narrow-minded.

The most complete portrait of Telford at Abingdon Street comes from Mitchell, and it provides a frame in which the fragments gained from his various correspondents sit very comfortably.[10]

> Telford did not go into what is called 'Society', but he was always delighted to see his friends at home. Occasionally he had dinner parties consisting of gentlemen chiefly connected with his works in progress, such as Sir Henry Parnell, afterwards Lord Congleton, Milne, Secretary, afterwards Chief Commissioner of the Board of Works, Admiral Sir Pulteney Malcolm, and General Pasley. Southey and Campbell the poets were also frequent guests, and he had visits from agents and engineers in the country. Telford was the soul of cheerfulness, and used to keep his guests in a roar of laughter. He had a joke for every little circumstance, and he was full of anecdote. His ordinary manner to a stranger was that of a happy, cheerful, clear-headed, upright man; but any attempt to impose on him, or any exhibition of meanness or unfair dealing, called forth expressions of stern indignation and severe invective.

His friends, then, were not exclusively drawn from the ranks of engineers, and he took a lively interest in a wide variety of topics. He certainly never lost his early love for poetry, and later in life put up funds for the publication of a biography of his early hero, Robert Burns. But it was engineering that dominated his life, and he was an enthusiastic supporter of the profession, which brings us to one of the last of the controversies surrounding Telford's life: the formation of the Institution of Civil Engineers.

A Society of Civil Engineers was formed in 1771, with John Smeaton among its first members and most active supporters. At his death, it was renamed 'The Smeatonian Society of Civil Engineers' in his honour. There were regular meetings where members could exchange ideas in a sociable setting, which one would have thought might have appealed to Telford. Although Gibb claims he was a member, but did not actually choose to attend, there is in fact no record of his ever having been elected. Why not? By the early years of the nineteenth century, he was certainly one of Britain's most highly regarded engineers. Charles Hadfield has suggested that it must be because he would never agree to belong to any organisation in which he was not himself pre-eminent, and in particular he would not join knowing that Jessop had a senior position on the committee. He does concede that there might have been an alternative reason. John Rennie had been elected in 1785, at the young age of twenty-four and at a time when Telford was thinking of a fulfilling career not in engineering but in architecture. So that by the time Telford was eligible for membership, Rennie was a well-established member – and there was no love lost between them. When Rennie's wife died, Telford wrote to James Watt:[11]

> I am truly sorry to find that Mr Rennie has suffered so serious and distressing a loss, and I am also sorry to inform you that his conduct prevents me from benefiting by his acquaintance. Altho' I never had any connection with him in business or ever intentionally did anything to injure or interfere with him, I, in every quarter, hear of his treating my character with a degree of illiberality not very becoming. This is so marked a part of his conduct, that I really believe it does him a serious injury and proves serviceable to me. As I am desirous of not suffering in your good opinion, I mention this with a view to counteracting any insinuations which may be advanced to my disadvantage.

If that was the situation between the two, it was hardly an encouragement to Telford to pop round to the Smeatonians for a pleasant social evening, whatever the professional advantages. Hadfield acknowledges this, but has his own explanation.[12] 'Is it not therefore a fair assumption that the second engineer of the canal mania did not at all like the way his friend, and to some degree his mentor, Jessop, had been treated by Telford on the Ellesmere Canal?' Well, no, it does not seem a fair assumption. The mistreatment, if that is what it was, cannot be dated back before the opening of Pontcysyllte, when Telford is said to have claimed unfair credit. Yet Telford was writing about a long-running grievance some six months before the opening. Once again, it seems that there is no way of knowing precisely why Telford did not belong to the Smeatonian, but there are many far stronger reasons than an argument about Jessop's reputation. It may even be that the simplest explanation of all provides the answer: an invitation was given to him when he was on one of his many frantic rounds of work and travel and the idea of joining a club which met fortnightly in London might have seemed too absurd to contemplate.

There is also something of a question mark over the Smeatonians, a suggestion that they were too exclusive, with membership limited to a highly select few, and that there was rather more of a social than a technological emphasis to the meetings. There was a feeling among at least some engineers that a different kind of body was needed to promote the welfare of what was, after all, an occupation that had only recently come to be regarded as a profession rather than a trade. In particular, they felt that while it was all very well for the senior members of the profession to get together, there was also a real need for a body where young engineers could find out about new advances in technology and hear details of the most recent techniques.

It was on Christmas Eve 1817 that a group of engineers led by one of Telford's young men, Robinson Palmer, met in London to discuss the idea of a new organisation. The first formal meeting was held at the Kendal Coffee House in Fleet Street on 2 January 1818. There were only six present but they agreed a set of rules, including one that limited membership to engineers aged between twenty and thirty-five, 'so as to prevent reserve in the young members', which sounds remarkably like a declaration that they wanted something a good deal less stuffy than they would find among the Smeatonians. It also made them sound like a bunch of Young Turks, rebelling against the establishment, and other young engineers, mindful of their careers, might not have felt too keen to rush along to join up behind their banner. So, for two years, the society languished, but out of their discussions a far greater idea was born, for an Institution of Civil Engineers that would be a leading organisation, open to all qualified engineers. It was not, however, going to get started, let alone succeed, without the addition of some gravitas. At a meeting on 25 January 1820, the rule books were hastily rewritten with the age limitations thrown out. It was then agreed to ask Telford to be the president.

In their letter to him, the members set out their aims.[13] Firstly, to establish engineering as a profession, since in Britain it was 'only taught as a trade' and public confidence was being eroded 'by the presumption of unskilful and illiterate persons taking upon themselves the name'. Secondly, it would be a means of passing on knowledge and sharing experience. As the writers noted, 'much inconvenience is suffered from the dearth of publications of tried practical men, and from the scarcity of means of obtaining any advantage from experience'. Telford replied, with what sounds suspiciously like mock modesty that he would accept the post 'until a fitter person can be selected'.[14] He went on to make an immediate practical offer of a collection of books to form the core of a library. In the inaugural address of 21 March 1820, he set out the basic principles of the new Institution.

In foreign countries similar establishments are instituted by government, and their members and proceedings are under its control; but here, a different course being adopted, it becomes incumbent on each individual member to feel that the very existence and prosperity of the institution depend in no small degree on his personal conduct and exertions; and the merely mentioning the circumstances will, I am convinced, be sufficient to command the best efforts of the present and future members, always keeping in mind that talents and respectability are preferable to numbers, and that from too easy and promiscuous admission, unavoidable, and not infrequently incurable, inconveniences perplex most societies.

Early meetings were held in coffee houses, and there were so few members that, at first they were all able to dine at Abingdon Street before the meetings. The institution's growth was slow, and Telford's interest in it was crucial to its development. When Rickman was preparing the material that Telford had left behind for his memoirs, he wrote to many who knew him and one who responded was George May, who gave this account of the early years.[15]

Mr Telford is justly entitled to be considered the *founder* of the Institution, and to his patronage alone it owed its ultimate advancement and prosperity – From his extensive intercourse with Engineers in every part of the Kingdom, he was enabled immediately after undertaking the office of President to bring a great accession of Members, and thus confer upon it at once the character of a fixed and widespread association ... Indeed, the interest he took in its success, as I well remember, was extreme; scarcely any business, be it ever so important, was allowed to interfere with his regular attendance upon its Meetings; and his presence was no doubt one of the chief causes of attraction to others in the infant state of the Society.

Soon, the Institution grew to the point when it could look for its own premises, starting in Buckingham Street, London. Telford gave few papers himself, but regularly contributed to the discussions. And on looking through the list of topics covered, there is more than a hint that he primed his young men to give voice to his own preoccupations, especially on one of his favourite topics, the relative merits of canal and railway transport. From the first, the Institution took its objective of spreading information very seriously, and one method was to persuade working engineers to write accounts of what they were doing and the problems they were solving. The result is a unique archive, which, whatever its value to the practical engineers of the day, has been a gold mine to historians. The other main aim of attaining professional status was given immense impetus in 1818, when the Institution was granted a Royal Charter.

No 'fitter person' was ever found, nor looked for, and there is no record of Telford ever offering his resignation. But there were always battles to be fought. There was still a sense that engineering was not quite a profession, not really respectable: professionals did not get their hands dirty. In 1834, a proposal was put forward that the secretary should not be someone who made a living from engineering, so that he could be a disinterested party. This was too much for one member, John Fovey, who wrote to Telford in great indignation. To suggest that a practising engineer would inevitably put self-interest first was a slur on the whole profession – and the lack of technical knowledge was precisely what was wrong with the present secretary. He ended witheringly: 'Amateur Engineers I have never met with, any more than Amateur lawyers or physicians.'[16]

Telford was not a founding member of the Institution, but it would never have succeeded had it been left to a group of young men, however enthusiastic. It needed the blessing of one of the leading engineers of the day, and none stood higher in general esteem than Thomas Telford. He could, as many have done when offered presidencies of societies, allowed them to use his name and left it at that. He did so very much more – in spite of his age and a still desperately hectic working life, he could be said to be among the most active of members. It must have been highly encouraging to the young, and even not so young, members who came along to their first meeting to find the president there in person, talking over ideas and arguing about new methods and materials. That what began with half a dozen young engineers in a coffee house became one of the main professional bodies is due in very large measure to Thomas Telford. It was by no means the least of his achievements.

Although London provided him with a home, and the nearest thing he was ever to enjoy to a social life, it provided him with surprisingly little work. He had dreamed of building a bridge over the Thames, but it was John Rennie who was to be given the three new Thames crossings, Southwark Bridge, the original Waterloo Bridge, and the one that Telford himself had hoped for, London Bridge. His advice was asked for and given on a number of schemes. As far back as 1806, he had become involved in problems of water supply when he was appointed engineer to Glasgow Waterworks, and had set up a system where water from the Clyde was pumped through filter beds. He also advised on similar problems in Edinburgh. Now London turned to him and he did his usual thorough job, but made it quite clear that there was no quick, cheap solution on offer. That was not what politicians wanted to hear, and prevarication took the place of action. That he spent so long in London working on proposals which were destined never to be put into action was in no way due to any incompetence on his part, but was entirely dictated by the vagaries of political life. An idea that had seemed all sweetness and sound reason to one administration could become anathema to the next. He was probably not very concerned. It meant that London became a place where he could return from his labours, meet old friends and, for the first time in his life, sit down by his very own fireside.

CHAPTER FIFTEEN

Railways versus Canals

Telford had very set views on railways. He was quite prepared to accept that freight waggons running on iron rails had a very real place in building up a national transport system – and that place was to link canals and navigable rivers to areas which could not be reached by boat. Just such an area was the high Cotswold plateau, and in 1821 local interests received an Act authorising them to build a railway to link the market town of Moreton-in-Marsh with the Avon at Stratford. Coal would be brought down from the Midlands coalfield along the Stratford-upon-Avon Canal and sent on up the line, while agricultural produce for the industrial towns could make the return journey. Telford was consulted on various points, but his own interests and prejudices soon came to the fore. He was asked to adjudicate between different types of track.[1] The first, suggested by Thomas Brewin of Halesowen, was for a line using edge rails developed for use with flanged wheels – the system in use on modern railways – which would allow for the possibility of using either horses or steam locomotives on the line. Telford would have none of that; railways were acceptable, but not locomotives. The second type, proposed by John Greaves, was for a plateway, using L-shaped cast-iron rails, the system widely used on tramways at that time. This was much more to the great man's liking, and the Stratford and Moreton Railway was duly built as a line to be worked by horses. It was a grand affair in its way, and included an important viaduct of eight arches across the Avon at Stratford. The bridge itself still stands, though the line has long since gone, one of the very few monuments to Telford's involvement in any positive sense in the new railway age. Rather more important for the future, one of the chief promoters and also the engineer of the line was a local businessman from Henley-in-Arden, William James, who was to break with the tramway faction to become an ardent supporter of the steam railway.

It was typical of this period that no one was at all certain as to how valuable railways were, nor which was the best way forward. The north-east of England was the area which had seen a widespread use of tramways, joining collieries to rivers, and it was among the first areas to make serious use of the steam locomotive. William Hedley began designing and building engines as early as 1813 – *Puffing Billy* is the most famous example – and he was soon followed by a local colliery engineer, George Stephenson. So one might have thought that this was the one area where Telford's views would be of little interest. Then, a proposal was put forward for a transport route linking Newcastle to Carlisle, with two options under consideration. The one which brought Telford in was for a ship canal. He looked over the proposals, declared that the expense would be enormous, and that because of the busy north–south road traffic which would have made swing or lifting bridges impractical, the scheme would not work. So he came down firmly on the side of a rail connection.[2] Then the other question automatically came up: horse or steam? Even the local news-papers doubted the value of the new invention, roundly declaring that the advantages of the machine had 'either through interest or igno-rance, been greatly overrated'.[3] The line was authorised by Parliament, but with a proviso that only horses should be used – a case which Telford still felt prepared to argue when the line was opened, and he was again asked to report on traction.[4] It is worth noting that Telford's first report on the Newcastle and Carlisle Railway came out in the same year that was to see the opening of the world's first public steam railway, the Stockton and Darlington. Telford had done the Newcastle and Carlisle Company no favours in helping to persuade them to turn away from the steam engine. He was soon fighting the same battle across the country in an increasingly desperate attempt to promote the canal interest in the face of a rapidly expanding railway lobby.

Today, it is easy to see that the railway movement was unstoppable, but it was by no means obvious even in 1825, when the Stockton and Darlington opened. This was still, in fact if not in name, a colliery line writ large. There was, it is true, a passenger service, but that was no more than a stage coach with flanged wheels that was pulled by horses.

The Holyhead Road winding its way through the Nant Ffrancon Pass in a somewhat romanticised Snowdonia. (*Gwynedd Archives Service*)

The bridge across the Menai Straits as seen from the Anglesey side, 1830. (*Bodleian Library, University of Oxford, 3995 d. i. No 342*)

A stagecoach on the road near Penmaenmawr between Conwy and Bangor. The picture shows the huge retaining walls. Down at sea level is the Chester and Holyhead Railway. This section was opened in 1848. (*Gwynedd Archives Service*)

One of Telford's most elegant iron bridges over the Severn at Holt Fleet, photographed c. 1890. (*Worcestershire Record Office*)

The excavation of the basins for St Katharine's Docks in 1827. (*Museum of London, PLA Collection*)

The opening of St Katharine's Docks, 25 October 1828, with the *Elizabeth* dressed overall and coming into the basin from the river. (*Museum of London, PLA Collection*)

A barge makes its way down the Sankey Canal while a train passes overhead on the Liverpool and Manchester Railway: not a sight to please Thomas Telford. *(National Railway Museum/ Science and Society Picture Library)*

Telford's challenge to the railway age: the deep Grub Street cutting on the Birmingham & Liverpool Junction Canal, now the Shropshire Union. *(Archive of British Waterways)*

The once-great covered docks of Ellesmere Port, with narrow boats, barges and a small coastal steamer. *(Archive of British Waterways)*

Broomielaw Bridge, Glasgow, is the centrepiece of the picture, but perhaps even more important were the river improvements which enabled ships to reach the heart of the city. *(Institution of Civil Engineers)*

(Left) Telford's startling Gothic design for the Avon Gorge at Clifton. He lost the competition to the young Brunel. *(Reproduced by permission of the Librarian, University of Bristol)*

(Below) Telford's last great Scottish bridge: Dean Bridge, Edinburgh, was designed to open up new land for development across the Water of Leith. *(By courtesy of Edinburgh City Libraries)*

Telford near the end of his life, sketched by William Brockedon in 1834.
(By courtesy of the National Portrait Gallery, London)

The first locomotives, *Locomotion* and *Hope*, were of a pattern familiar in north-eastern collieries and strictly reserved for low-speed freight haulage. Anyone who has seen the replica *Locomotion*, now on the museum site at Beamish, will find a somewhat alarming-looking machine, with piston and valve rods popping up and down like an over-animated sewing machine, right in front of the driver's nose. Riding on the locomotive itself is an interesting, if unnerving, experience as the vertical cylinders produce a bouncing effect and you seem to progress down the track in a rhythmic rise and fall. The engineering of the line itself was very much on the tramway principle, with level sections worked by the locomotives, and slopes overcome by cable haulage up and down inclined planes. The steam engine itself was inefficient, speeds were low and the railway seemed to offer little that was not available to the horse-drawn tramway, apart from a large coal bill. This was not a problem for colliery lines, where the cost of coal scarcely registered, but to many commentators it seemed to preclude a more general expansion of the system.

Telford was able to use the Institution of Civil Engineers as a forum for expressing his own views that canals were at least as efficient as railways in most circumstances and often a great deal more so. Henry Palmer conducted a series of experiments on the relative resistance to be overcome by a boat travelling through water and a waggon running on rails. He used a horse-drawn truck on the Hetton Colliery tramway and a boat on the Ellesmere Canal, measuring the forces on a dynamometer he had himself designed. He found little difference on the flat, but even the slightest gradient on the track produced a marked increase in resistance from the waggons. He summed up his own views in a letter that was just what Telford wanted to hear: 'The Railway men have circulated a great abundance of absurdities as to resistance on their railways, and nobody seems to have any confidence in the information they have collected.'[5] His own results he regarded as thoroughly scientific. What neither he nor Telford could foresee was the dramatic increase in locomotive efficiency that was to appear – and on a railway with which Telford himself was to be heavily involved.

The line was to link Liverpool and Manchester, and there is a pleasing irony about the first part of the story. It is generally agreed that the Bridgewater Canal of 1760 inaugurated the first wave of canal building, but it only received parliamentary assent in the face of fierce opposition from the older Irwell Navigation, who then commanded most of the

trade between the two centres. Now, the main opposition to the railway
was the Bridgewater Canal, who in turn complained about the unfair
competition the upstart represented. George Stephenson was the engineer, as he had been on the Stockton & Darlington, but here he was tackling work on a very different scale. His first plans received an
embarrassing mauling in Parliament, when it soon became clear that
Stephenson had relied too much on others and that much of the surveying work was hopelessly inaccurate. Things were so bad that for a time it
seemed the whole project would be handed over to the Rennies, but that
soon fell through. When work finally got under way in 1826, Stephenson
was very much the man in charge.

The line involved heavy engineering works, including tunnels, a cutting through solid rock at the Liverpool end, embankments and
viaducts, including a lofty structure soaring above the old river navigation of the Sankey Canal. There was one difficulty, however, that sur-
passed all others – the crossing of the great bog, Chat Moss. Stephenson
had no experience of work on this scale, and Chat Moss seemed almost
impassable. All attempts at drainage failed: the black mud simply oozed
back into the trenches. Eventually, the line was to be built by creating a
'raft' of birch wood and heather. But in the early days, there was a real
worry that the work was not going well, nor was it being properly managed. Telford may not have had much experience of railways, but no one
knew more about tackling major civil-engineering projects, and when it
came to the choice of an engineer to make a report on the line, his was
the obvious first name on the list.

At the end of November 1828, Telford sent one of his best men,
James Mills, to look over the works. He would have had a good idea
what to expect had it been a canal-construction site. The chief engineer would have been responsible for overseeing all the surveys from
which cost estimates would have been prepared. The work would then
have been parcelled up into large lots, which would have been offered
out to tender to established contractors. None of this, it soon
appeared, was happening on the railway. Mills found that Stephenson
appeared to be relying on a survey carried out before the Act was
passed by John Rennie and Charles Vignoles, and that everything was
based on their findings.[6]

> There is some difficulty in making out correctly the value of what is to do,
> for in truth there does not appear to be a single contract existing on the
> whole line. Stevenson [sic] seems to be the contractor for the whole, and
> to employ all the different people at such prices as he thinks proper to

give them, the company finding all Materials, not only rails and Waggons, but even Wheelbarrows and Planks &c.

When Telford produced his official report, he was even more scathing. He described how the work was not handed out to contractors, but put directly under the control of Stephenson's three principal assistants.[7]

> Each has 200 day men employed and pay them every fortnight as *Company*'s men for laying temporary roads, moving planks, driving piles and, in short, doing *every thing* but putting the stuff into the carts and barrows which is done by a set of men which is also under their direction and to whom they pay 3½ d per yard to 5s as they think it deserves.

He saw no hope of Chat Moss ever being crossed – a prediction which many others were making, but which Stephenson was destined to prove wrong. His method worked and his perseverance paid off. The other criticisms of expensive working methods and inefficiencies were more difficult to refute. The Railway Company did not even try but simply resorted to abuse, writing of Telford's report: 'a document than which one more abounding with inaccuracies and erroneous statements can hardly be conceived'.[8] If they thought the initial report was harsh, the undated reply was even more fierce.

> In reply to the observation that the Board rely upon the authority of their Engineer would it not have been better to have directed their Engineer to have compared his calculations with Mr Telford's. You will know however why the Board did not do this. You will know their Engineer is not capable of making the survey and it would have been more candid to have said that one of the Engineers Agents or Apprentices had made such statements to the Board.

One of the fascinations of following the story of the Liverpool and Manchester line is this clash between two great engineers whose careers briefly overlapped and who represent two very different traditions.

Telford had one other major criticism to make, and it certainly highlighted a glaring absurdity: no one had decided how the railway was to be run. One faction held that the answer was cable haulage over the whole route, a mind-boggling concept, another favoured the familiar tramway solution, and Stephenson was all for the steam locomotive. But was the steam locomotive up to the job? The issue was decided at the famous Rainhill Trials of 1829, when *Rocket*, designed and built by George Stephenson's son Robert, triumphantly carried the day, reaching the previously undreamed-of speed of 30 miles per hour. Its design features, especially the multi-tube boiler, offered immense scope for development, and would lead directly to the bigger, faster, more powerful locomotives of the future.

The success of *Rocket* and the railway as a whole, which was opened in 1830, gave a huge impetus to railway building. Even then Telford did not give in: he simply could not accept that the railway locomotive was as good as it appeared to be. He remained convinced that the canal boat was also capable of improvement, and could match anything the steam men could come up with. He set up a test tank for use with model boats, and enthused over the results.[9]

> I have during the last fortnight, been constantly engaged with experiments respecting the Velocity of Canal Passage Boats. The Canal, in the National Gallery, is 70 feet long, 4 feet wide and the depth of Water one foot. – I had a boat constructed of sheet Copper, agreeable to a Model furnished by Mr. Wood of Port Glasgow, 10 feet long and 9 inches wide, fitted with proper apparatus for trackage.
>
> Under these circumstances 250 Experiments were made with great accuracy, under the immediate management of Mr. Mcneil on whose talents I can confidently rely, and I am happy to say, that the results confirm your Statements respecting what has been experienced upon the Paisley Canal. – Numerous spectators witnessed the performances at the National Gallery, and I am convinced that such a sensation has been created, as to overpower the Railway Models with which the Gallery is encumbered.

But it was all far too late to stem the enthusiasm for railways. The problem lay, in any case, less with the boats than with the canals themselves.

The first wave of canal building in England was dominated by the figure of James Brindley. His preferred building method was contour cutting: following the natural curves of the landscape to avoid difficult and expensive earthworks. This can be seen at its most extravagant on the southern section of the Oxford Canal and on the Staffs & Worcester Canal. It was also a technique that he used on what was in many ways the most successful canal of them all, the Birmingham. When it was built in 1767, shares had cost £140; twenty-five years later they were changing hands for £1,170. There was an immense trade in coal, not least supplying the new industries that were springing up on its banks, most famously the Boulton and Watt works at Soho. But it was built to the old Brindley style, wobbling and staggering across the landscape like a drunk at closing time. What had been the latest thing in the 1760s looked sadly out of date at the birth of the railway age.

This was not the only problem that Brindley bequeathed to a later generation.

In 1766, he was appointed chief engineer for the most ambitious canal scheme of the age, the Trent & Mersey or Grand Trunk Canal. He faced one problem that was to have a profound effect on the English canal system: he had to drive a tunnel for nearly two miles through Harecastle Hill, near Stoke-on-Trent. The first canal on which he had worked was the Bridgewater, designed to take Mersey barges, roughly 70 feet long by 14 feet wide (21.3 by 4.3 metres). The idea of building a tunnel to that width was more than he could contemplate, so he decided to halve the width. And he reasoned that if the largest vessel that could go through the tunnel was to be 7 feet wide, then there was no point in wasting money on wide locks. So the narrow canal system was born and with it the familiar narrow boat. There was nothing much to be done about that, but Harecastle tunnel had become a serious nuisance. It had no towpath, so boats had to be slowly legged through by boatmen lying on their backs, painstakingly walking their feet along the tunnel walls. And it was strictly one-way traffic: no boat could head north until the tunnel was clear of south-bound traffic and vice versa. It had become a serious bottleneck on a vital route.

Telford found himself with serious problems to solve if two of the most important routes in the whole system of communications were going to offer transport routes appropriate for the nineteenth century. In January 1822, he turned his attention to Harecastle. John Rennie had already reported on the tunnel, and reading his reports, one is amazed that anyone ever ventured into it and, if they did, that they made it out to the other side. When one reads of holes in the wall, gaps in the brickwork and so on, one has to imagine what that would have meant to the men legging through in the pitch dark. Here is a section of the report that gives the flavour of the whole.[10]

> In many places the roof is not more than 6 feet above the ordinary level of the water ... in some places it is too narrow, in others crooked, and generally speaking the brickwork which forms the bottom, sides & top of the Tunnel is not more than 9 inches thick, it has throughout been made with bad mortar, so that in all the brickwork under water ... the mortar is as soft as clay.

The tunnel ran close to coal measures, and the colliers had cheerily banged side tunnels through to the face, so that sections were in danger of collapse. Nothing happened immediately, but two years later, Telford was called in. He agreed with Rennie, stating very firmly: 'The tunnel as regards general intercourse is, in several parts, too narrow and too low, and has certainly from long experience been found quite inadequate for the business transacted. The only effectual remedy, simple and practically useful, is another Tunnel.'

Eventually, in 1824, almost four years after receiving Rennie's devastating report, the company finally gave the go ahead. It was agreed that the old tunnel should be fully repaired and a new one built alongside it. Boats could then go one way down the old, while boats going in the opposite direction could use the new – with the added advantage that Telford's tunnel would be considerably easier to use, as it was built to a more generous size, with a towpath all the way through. A tunnel does not sound as interesting as a whole canal, and building it seems much less of an achievement, but it stands in reality as being among the most impressive of Telford's canal works.

Brindley's low, crooked, narrow hole in the hill took eleven years to complete, and the engineer himself, who had proudly claimed to be able to finish it in five, was dead before it was open. Telford's tunnel was far larger, ran straight and true for 2926 yards (2675 metres) and was finished in three. The scale of the works was immense – far greater than those of James Brindley. Once the line had been surveyed, shafts were sunk down to the depth of the tunnel, and that turned out to be hard work.[11]

> The ground is of different and various kinds such as Rock, Sand Coal Measures and other kinds of Earth – very tedious to encounter with. The Rock I find to be extremely hard, some of it in my opinion is much harder than ever any Tunnel has been driven in before – excepting the one that is executed by the side of it.

On the strength of that, he upped his estimate from £60,000 to £82,473 15s. There were to be seventeen shafts in all. At each one, a horse gin had to be built on top, a simple device for raising spoil from the workings, in which a horse walking round a circular track turned a winding drum through wooden gearing. The gin itself cost £50, three horses were needed for continuous work day and night at a cost of £26 each and the actual cost of sinking varied from 21 shillings (£1.05) a yard for 6-foot shafts to 55 shillings (£2.75) a yard for 9 foot. The various shafts were linked by railway at the top of the hill, and lines were also laid in the tunnel itself as the headings were gradually dug out from the foot of each shaft and from the two entrances. Once excavation had advanced a short way, a brick lining was built inside the tunnel. Steam engines worked day and night to pump out water, and the company also had its own brickworks which had to turn out an estimated 7 million bricks.

It is difficult now to imagine what the scene must have been like during construction, but the author was fortunate enough to be able to see the tunnel when it was drained for repairs in 1977 and to have a chance to inspect the construction in detail. The first impression was how very similar it was to a mine – hardly surprising, as the same technology was used for both. The brickwork was beautifully constructed, and a number of the old iron formers on which the arch was built were discovered, and setting these against the present arch showed just how well the interior had survived. The bricks themselves were shallow, flat and very hard – and the modern engineers had no hesitation in copying the Telford design. Watching modern workmen struggling with pneumatic drills to cope with the hard rock where repairs were needed made me appreciate the efforts of men who had to drill holes by hand for a simple charge of black powder. Above ground in the 1820s, a small village was growing.[12]

> Some small dwelling Houses, Stables and Workshops have been constructed on the summit of the Tunnel line by which the workmen and horses are accommodated conveniently for their different operations in which they are employed – a matter of no inferior consequence in saving time and trouble, and avoiding unnecessary exposure in bad weather.

At the same time that all this was going on, the company had decided to improve their water supply by constructing a new reservoir 3½ miles (5.5 kilometres) away at Knypersley, between Stoke-on-Trent and Biddulph. As usual, Telford selected one of his own men to act as resident engineer, to be in charge of both tunnel and reservoir. The Trent & Mersey Company, who had been initially reluctant to authorise any expenditure at all, proved equally reluctant to pay now that they had authorised it. They not only quibbled about paying the resident engineer James Potter's salary, but withheld the money for a whole year while they argued the toss. Once the news reached Telford, he at once stepped in and laid down the law.[13]

> ... the proper management of the tunnel Works joined with those of the Knipersley Reservoir including the expense to which any person having this charge is invariably subjected is a service deserving a Salary of £500 a Year, and that this was what would have been required by any other duly

qualified person I could have provided, and this more especially when there is such an unusually great demand for persons of this description.

Altho' it has so happened that Mr James Potter a very young man has been appointed to this charge, and that his Salary may appear large for his first Essay, yet as by the due exertion of talents and unwearied assiduity, aided by the experience and judgement of his father, the whole of the complicated and in many instances dangerous operations have been arranged and in every respect carried on in a well regulated and successful manner, under the management of persons in whom the Company have cause to place confidence, I do not see any reason why a less remuneration is due than what a stranger would have required.

Having settled that point, the company then tackled Telford himself, objecting to the fact that he was taking on other work on other canals. Telford immediately offered to resign from the Trent & Mersey instead, at which point the stout party duly collapsed. In a way, one sympathises with the company. They had just the one canal that engaged all their interest, and probably felt everyone else should share their attitude. And Telford, as ever, was busy on myriad schemes. But even James Potter's father, Samuel, who had been around a long time, was not above the occasional chiding remark: 'I hope you will excuse me from troubling you but I feared that owing to the numerous engagements which you have at this season, you had forgotten us.'[14]

The work on the whole went well, though there was trouble with quicksand at the northern end, and by the spring of 1827 all was ready for inspection. Telford was delighted, and noted how straight it was, adding very justly, 'a circumstance very uncommon in such works'. Work also appeared to be going ahead well at the reservoir, where the main task was removing the very large amount of alluvial deposit before a firm footing could be found for the holding embankment. The work was finished at much the same time as the tunnel, but in 1828, disaster struck, with 'a considerable escape of water ... through the Masonry of the Wall at the discharging Pipes: great alarm has been excited throughout the neighbourhood, as to the safety of the Work'.[15]

Telford at once gave orders for the reservoir to be drained for inspection, and a sorry state of affairs was revealed. Reservoirs, like canals, were kept waterproof by a layer of puddled clay, but with the whole reservoir earthworks settling and sinking, water had got behind the clay and begun to break it. Telford arranged for the necessary remedial work to be done, and then there came the post mortem. What had gone wrong? The full report of September suggested the fault lay with the foundations; they had settled unevenly, creating stresses and pressure which, combined with exceptionally wet weather, had led to the floods. It was generally agreed it would have been wiser to have let everything stabilise before letting in the water. No blame was attached to the engineer, but James Potter had the job of explaining the position to the Annual General Assembly – 'and rather a noisy meeting it was' as he wryly noted to Telford.[16] In the event, all went well, and the reservoir now forms the centrepiece of a country park, with no hint of the dramas of an earlier age.

While the Trent & Mersey were still dithering about whether to start work on the tunnel or not, Telford turned his attention to the Birmingham Canal. If he did not like what he saw at Harecastle, he was if anything even less impressed by Birmingham.[17]

> Upon inspection I found adjacent to this great and flourishing town a canal little better than a crooked ditch with scarcely the appearance of a haling-path, the horses frequently sliding and staggering in the water, the haling-lines sweeping the gravel into the canal and the entanglement at the meeting of the boats incessant; while at the locks at each end of the short summit crowds of boatmen were always quarrelling, or offering premiums for a preference of passage, and the mine owners, injured by the delay, were loud in their just complaints.

The canal had been improved over the years. The short summit at Smethwick in Brindley's day was a very Duke of York affair, with boats climbing up through three locks to the top of the hill and back down another three at the opposite end. In 1790, a cutting removed part of the problem. The canal as a whole was still something of a shambles, with a switchback progress that involved back-pumping to return water to the higher levels to refill the locks that had just emptied. Add to this the confusion of a narrow waterway with two-way traffic, all relying on the same inadequate towpath, and the immense detours that Brindley took round every piece of rising ground, and it did not take a genius to see there was room for improvement. It did, however, take immense boldness and self-confidence to put forward the scheme that Telford now proposed.

He wanted a brand-new canal to run from the Farmer's Bridge locks at one side of the Birmingham plateau to Wolverhampton, where the canal fell down another flight of locks to a junction with the Staffs & Worcester Canal. This new canal was to represent something close to the Telford ideal. It was to be broad and deep, with towpaths to either side so that boats would never again need to unknit a tangle of ropes. It was to be straight and to stay on one level, though that would involve heavy engineering works, with the canal carried through the high ground in a deep cutting. There was to be nothing to impede the smooth movement of traffic.

The new Birmingham Canal was designed to slice through the middle of the old sinuous canal, leaving its bends as loops off the main line – an essential feature since many of the canal company's most important customers had sites on the old line. That left an interesting problem to be solved: what was the best and cheapest way of getting the new towpath over the top of the old canal and any side arms along the way? The answer was found in one of the earliest applications of a mass-production technique to a transport system. Telford went to a new but very enterprising company, the Horseley Iron Works, on a nearby canal-side site at Tipton. They had only built their first furnace in 1809–10, but they soon showed themselves both efficient and innovative, and developed a speciality in marine steam engines and iron-hulled boats. For the canal bridges, they produced a standard design that could be reproduced over and over again. It consisted of two arches, each with the handrail as an integral casting, which could be joined by a central locking plate. The actual footway in between was built out of iron plates, bolted together. The success of the scheme is clear from the many surviving examples, with the maker's name still proudly displayed on the arch.

At Smethwick, the canal was crossed by a bridge where the cutting was at its deepest. If it looks familiar that is not surprising, for it used exactly the same design as for Mythe Bridge across the Severn, right down to the decorative pattern of pointed arches carved into the piers. It was named Galton Bridge after one of the Birmingham Canal Navigation Committee members. Near this point, modern visitors can see three quite distinct levels of canal: the upper, the old Brindley summit, now quite dried up; slightly lower down is Smeaton's improved line; and at the bottom is the wide, straight line pushed through by Telford. The second problem was a necessary canal connection to a steam pumping station, supplying the old summit. The Engine Arm had to be taken across on a brand-new aqueduct, and here Telford indulged his taste for ornamentation. Essentially, it is a simple cast-iron aqueduct carried on a single span. But Telford had not entirely lost his architectural ambitions, and he was a keen follower of the latest trends and fashions. Classicism was going out and Gothic coming in, so he added decoration above the ribs of the arch to carry the towpath in the shape of a long row of pointed arches. The effect is actually quite pleasing, but he would be astonished to hear that many people today find the simple majesty of Galton Bridge far more appealing than the rather fussy aqueduct.

The deep cuttings are still an imposing feature, and John Rickman, who went to see the workings, has given us a clear idea of how they were constructed. One of the greatest problems was the removal of the spoil from the bottom of the excavations to the banks at the top, and Rickman described three systems, all variations on the techniques used on the Caledonian Canal (see pp. 97–9). In the simplest, a man walked up a sloping plank balancing a barrow load of spoil which was hauled by a horse. The rope passed through a block, and was then attached to an empty barrow which a second man now guided back down again. The more sophisticated version consisted of a horizontal staging, raised and lowered along a railed track. In an improvement on this Caledonian-derived system, larger stages were built to hold two barrows, with a loaded weight of up to 4 hundredweight (200 kilograms), which needed two horses working a winding drum. To supply the new canal, a large reservoir was built at Rotton Park.

To Telford, all this proved that canals were still capable of development and there was no need at all to even contemplate their replacement as the main freight routes of the country. But the clamour for railways could not be stilled, and as new proposals came forward, so he made brave attempts to counter them in a final burst of creative energy. He was not unduly concerned with lines such as the Stockton and Darlington, which provided a source of cargoes to the shipping on the Tees, but when plans started to appear for a railway to link Liverpool and Birmingham he saw a direct threat to the canal interest. Birmingham was the prosperous heart of the English canal system, and anything that threatened trade there threatened the whole. The trouble was that although there was now a good modern link south to London, thanks to Jessop's Grand Junction Canal, the more northerly routes still depended on the first-generation, Brindley routes, through the wayward Staffs & Worcester to the Trent & Mersey and on to the Bridgewater.

One obvious short cut presented itself. Hanging down like a droopy dog's tail from the east–west trans-Pennine system was the Peak Forest Canal, which at Marple was only around 30 miles from the northern end of the newly improved Harecastle Tunnel on the Trent & Mersey. Telford surveyed a line that would pass through the prosperous silk town of Macclesfield. It began with a canal 'flyover', leaving the Trent & Mersey and immediately turning to cross it on a short aqueduct. There was one stop lock to control the movement of water between the two canals, but apart from that all the remaining twelve locks were grouped together in a single flight. Elsewhere, changes in level were avoided by the use of cuttings and embankments. The Act was passed in 1826, though not without a scare, as some of the proprietors thought the unthinkable, and questioned whether a railway might not serve them better. Telford was content to leave the actual post of chief engineer to William Crosley. He had a far more demanding project of his own to contemplate.

He made his overriding concern clear in 1825 when the plan was forming, 'having, in the course of my investigations, with the view of rendering unnecessary, the proposed lines of railway between Birmingham & Liverpool, found it advisable to recommend making a canal between Autherley and Nantwich, and also an extension from Ellesmere Port along the shore of the River Mersey'.[18] The former was to be the Birmingham & Liverpool Junction Canal that was to run from the Staffs & Worcester, at a point very near the foot of the Wolverhampton locks, to link in with the Chester Canal at Nantwich and eventually to provide a through route to a major new inland port to be developed at Ellesmere Port on the Mersey. The extension along the Mersey was destined not to be built.

In essence, the thinking was the same as that behind the Birmingham – to take the shortest possible line, with as few stoppages as possible. And in some ways the task might have seemed easier. Travel the Birmingham today, and even now the industries crowd in, so that it seems it would have been a nightmare finding a route through a land where furnaces roared and engines hissed and puffed above deep mines. But many of those concerns had actively supported the canal, and others had arrived later precisely because of the facilities it offered. The Birmingham & Liverpool Junction was to run through a rural landscape, scarcely more than brushing against the few market towns met along the way. But it was not an empty land; not every landowner wanted a canal – and some had enough clout to make sure that if they had to have the wretched thing then it would be on their terms. Among these was Lord Anson. Look at the line of the canal on a modern map and you will find a long embankment marked just north of Gnosall Heath. But it does not go straight. It is set in a very considerable curve round Shelmore

Wood. That wood was the property of Lord Anson and the canal had to go round it. Given the subsequent history of this section of the canal, one has to say that a very high price was paid for aristocratic intransigence. What, after all, was the movement of half a million cubic yards of earth compared with the need to rear pheasants for His Lordship and his friends to pot at? On the route as a whole, the cost of land purchase came out at £100,000, a huge sum considering the cost for the entire project had been estimated at £400,000. The cost in extra work to keep the shooters happy was even more painful to bear.

The Act was approved in 1826 in the face of opposition from the Staffs & Worcester, who saw it as a threat to their own trade. One reason the canal companies were destined to fail in their opposition to railway competition was their inability to agree amongst themselves. Narrow self-interest ruled, to the extent that the Staffs & Worcester consistently refused to let one drop of their own precious water pass through to the upstart. This kind of wrangling did no one any favours, and added greatly to the cost of the new canal, which now had to make other, far more expensive, arrangements for water supply. But problems with landowners and rival companies were to prove as nothing compared with the difficulties that were about to appear in the land itself.

As always happens in such concerns, everything was begun in good spirits. At the first meeting after the passing of the Act, Telford proposed dividing the works of the main line into three lots, with work to start at the northern end.[19] At the next meeting, he reported that he had resurveyed the whole line, including a branch line to Newport to connect with the Shrewsbury canal system.[20] It had all been done with due care and attention, 'with two sets of levellers proving each other's work'. Work could begin and old friends and colleagues were brought in. The job of resident engineer went to Alexander Easton, a foregone conclusion given Telford's glowing recommendation of a man who had 'for 22 years been employed in similar works under my direction and in whose experience talents and integrity I have full confidence'. It would have been a brave committee man who objected. William Provis from Menai also joined the team. Telford was equally generous in praise of one of the contractors who had tendered for the work, John Wilson of Bangor, who had followed him down from the Caledonian to Holyhead.[21] Work was to start at the northern end, and Wilson agreed to take on all of the first two lots for £198,100.

The advantages of having a big contractor were soon apparent, for he went rapidly into action all the way down his section, so that by summer of 1827, Telford was able to report that there were 1600 men at work on the line.

Telford's plan was to take as direct a line as landowners would allow, keep locks grouped into flights as far as possible, and elsewhere iron out the vagaries of the landscape by 'cut and fill' – cutting deep through the hills and using the spoil to build up banks across the valleys. The line is indeed remarkably direct, and of the twenty-nine locks, all but four were grouped into flights at Tyrley, Adderley and Audlem. The cuttings and banks were on a scale greater than anything previously attempted. At first, all seemed to be going well, but in time, problems began to appear with all the earthworks. There were really two interrelated problems: the scale of the works and the nature of the ground. Telford was entering comparatively untried territory, and in the absence of any theoretical approach, he did what he had always done: advanced on the basis of previous experience. Among the ominous signs of trouble was the start of slippage on one of the big banks near Nantwich. He could only remark that the bank had been 'constructed with care and in the usual manner of canal works'.[22] Equally worrying were difficulties encountered in one of the deep cuttings at Woodseaves. When he planned the route, he had, as he admitted, no means of knowing what lay deep below the surface of the ground. Pragmatism had always ruled at the diggings: keep going until you meet a problem, such as quicksands in Harecastle tunnel, and when you meet it, solve it. The science of geology was in its infancy, and an engineer relied on personal judgement based on long experience. At Woodseaves, everything was far worse than Telford had imagined.[23]

> In performing this work a variety of different strata are met with consisting of a Marl, Clay and Rock so that in several places it is found necessary to cut out the Marl and support the Rock by dry stone walls and in other cases where the Rock is not so firm it is advisable to shape the sides 6 inches horizontal to one foot perpendicular.

It soon appeared that bad ground was only a part of the problem, for as the cutting went ever deeper so he found more and more difficulty in stabilising the sides. The days of easy optimism were clearly at an end.

All along the line there were troubles. The original intention had been to construct a 600-yard (550-metre) tunnel at Cowley, to be carried through the solid rock. But the rock proved to be such wretched stuff that most of the line of the tunnel had to be opened up to the sky, and in the end the actual tunnel was shortened to a modest 81 yards (74 metres). That was as nothing compared with the nightmare that was to follow as the men struggled to stabilise the cuttings and banks, and nothing was to give them more trouble than Shelmore Bank. How Telford must have cursed those miserable pheasants! Look at the Ordnance Survey map and you can see a contour line right on the most direct route, passing through the middle of the woods. That was precisely the route he would have chosen – and precisely the route that was denied him. Instead, he had to construct this immense, curving embankment stretching for a mile, high above the surrounding fields. Problems were not caused by lack of effort or bad workmanship. By the beginning of 1831, there were between three and four hundred men on the site, and up to seventy horses bringing the waggon-loads of spoil. The trouble was that the earth would not stay where it was put. Telford diagnosed the problem: 'at this stage, the rich marl of which this mound is composed was crushed and dissolved by its own weight which in some places squeezed out the sides to a considerable extent'.[24] The fault was, as he saw it, simply one of using the wrong sort of soil, so he ordered that, in future, a drier, sandy soil should be brought from another part of the workings and used instead. This, he was sure, would prove the answer. It was to prove only the first of a number of suggestions, always presented with an optimistic forecast of success.

A year later, the bank was still slipping, though there was some talk of building a narrow channel on top, wide enough to take one boat, but Telford argued that it was better to delay the opening 'three or four months' when everything was sure to be ready. Sadly, this was to be another of those optimistic forecasts. It was all very dispiriting, and slippage problems in the cuttings, particularly Grub Street, added to the general air of frustration. And to make matters worse, the endless years of work were taking their toll on the engineer, whose great strength and resolve were at last beginning to weaken. In January 1833, he was unable to present his annual report to the committee, and it was left to Easton to suggest what might be done at Shelmore. He proposed what was, in effect, a temporary wooden aqueduct sitting on top of the bank, but no one seemed impressed. It was, in any case, quite clear that the concern now lacked a chief engineer at a most critical period, and, with Telford's assent, a new man was brought in, William Cubitt. He went over the whole ground and, in general, found everything to be in a most satisfactory state. He, like his predecessor, was confident he had diagnosed the problem and found the solution. It all sounded eminently reasonable, though parts of it had a familiar ring.[25]

> Soil at the bottom of too weak a nature to keep it firm and support the weight of the upper part; and consequently as the top is put on, the sides slip out and would continue so to do, to an indefinite extent and for an indefinite length of time were no changes to be made to the qualities of the materials and the modes of putting them on.

He did, however, have one new suggestion. He was going to lay much heavier material on top of the bank, which would then sink down, forcing the poor material out to form a solid base. That would do the trick. Telford returned briefly in 1833, but was quite content to let Cubitt continue his work on The Great Bank, as it had become known.

Telford was to make just one more visit to the canal. He was seventy-seven years old but still determined to play his part and to do what he could, so he appeared before the committee to deliver his final report.[26]

> Having for the last two years from the state of my health been unable to pay personal attention to the practical operations upon the Canal this duty has been performed by Mr. William Cubitt with whom I have co operated as often as health would permit but as that has been in some measure restored I have taken the earliest opportunity of accompanying him on a general inspection.

There was no good news: the bank was not ready, the opening was postponed yet again. Poor Cubitt's optimism had now evaporated as well, and in his next report all he could say with bewildered sadness was that the work 'has hitherto defied all our calculations as to the time of the completion'. But the work did finally come to an end, and the canal was opened on 2 March 1835. Telford was not alive to see it.

The troubles that beset the Birmingham & Liverpool were those that can happen when something bold and new is tried. It frustrated the men of the day, but others were to learn from it, most particularly the new generation of railway engineers. How horrified Telford would have been to hear that one of those who took embanking skills into the new age was William Cubitt. And how saddened he would have been to find that this canal, which was meant to prove that railways were an unnecessary luxury, should in a few years become part of a larger system, the Shropshire Union Railway and Canal Company, and that would in turn fall to the mighty L.M.S. But he had much to be proud of, and proud he was. He designed the lock cottages, and took a special pleasure in the grandest of them all, close to the junction with the belligerent Staffs & Worcester. It was to be especially fine in order 'to awaken in the public a sense of the superiority in the new canal compared with the old'. Grander by far was the new dock complex that was to form a new northern terminus beside the Mersey at Ellesmere Port. Previously, it had been little more than a basin with locks down to the river, but now he designed an immense complex of warehouses, built out on arches across the water, so that boats could float in underneath for loading and unloading in the dry. A disastrous fire in the 1970s left only a fraction of the old buildings standing, but those that are left have provided a home to an important canal-boat museum. And there was to be one place where Telford can be forgiven a little self-aggrandisement, for the canal crossed the line of the Holyhead Road. The aqueducts were, like the Horseley bridges, a standard design in cast iron, but this one is marked by handsome stone pillars at the ends, and cast into the centre is Telford's name with the letters announcing his two recently acquired honours, Fellow of the Royal Society and Fellow of the Royal Society of Edinburgh. They were honours he richly deserved. The whole canal stands as a tribute to his daring genius, but it was not quite the last project of his working life.

CHAPTER SIXTEEN

The End of the Road

Telford's seventieth birthday came and went with no obvious signs of his appetite for work waning. His official reports were as crisp and businesslike as ever. The old juggling act of keeping a number of balls in the air still seemed to be working well. But to old friends he was prepared to admit to feelings of mortality. This was especially true of the Little family, as a new generation was to become party to his more private thoughts. In September 1829, he wrote to James Little in India.

> I hope your own health has not suffered from the India climate, its preservation is the most important of all objects; Since you left England, I have received some distant intimations that, even in this favourable Climate, existence is precarious; under that impression I have been endeavouring to contract my engagements, but have hitherto only imperfectly succeeded. I have this year been unavoidably led to extend them – not being able to resist the pressing applications of the two principal Cities of my native Country to furnish designs for their principal Bridges.

One of these bridges was to take him back to Edinburgh New Town, where he had worked as a young mason. Much had changed since those days. There had been a burst of building activity in the 1820s, and the developers had looked for their inspiration to Bath. The area had erupted in a rash of crescents and circuses, and even more exotic shapes. One of the most interesting of these was built on land owned by the Earl of Moray, with a crescent leading directly into an oval which in turn led to a dodecahedron. But the Moray Estate came to an abrupt halt where the land dropped away to a deep gorge with the little river, the Water of Leith, at the bottom. The obvious next step was to expand on the far side, but first the gorge needed to be bridged. There was an added incentive: the bridge could be used to carry the Great North Road on its way to Queensferry, the site of the ferry across the Firth of Forth. Local architects and designers were approached, but the trustees turned eventually to Telford, and so one of the two requests he was unable to resist landed on his desk.

The lure of the project was obvious. He could rarely turn down any appeal to his Scottish patriotism, and this was to be a monumental work in the capital city. His first idea was for three arches, each of a 90-foot (27.4-metre) span, the central arch rising 106 feet (32.3 metres) above the Water of Leith. Closer inspection showed that rock on the southern side of the gorge was likely to present problems, so there was a hasty redesign job and the three arches were increased to four. It was an interestingly original design, devised by Telford to reduce the weight of such a large structure. He borrowed one idea from Pontcysyllte, of using hollow piers, but the other feature seems to be entirely new. The main arches carrying the roadway spring to a height of 70 feet above the foundations and rise for 30 feet. Then, 20 feet higher, two outer arches were built with just a 10-foot rise to carry the two footpaths. This used considerably less masonry than if footpaths and road had all been carried on the same arches. Telford was all for decorating the sandstone to increase the effect, but the paymasters were quite content with the more austere design. It was opened in 1831, but the New Town stubbornly refused to spread north. Edinburgh was eventually to expand all the way to the Firth, but the old classical cohesion was ended.

The second Scottish project took him back to Broomielaw and Glasgow. He must have been delighted to see the effect of the work he had put in hand over twenty years before (see p. 117), for there was now deep water in the heart of Glasgow instead of shoals, and a newly acquired steam dredger had been set to work in 1824 to keep it that way. Here, he found the familiar problem of a river bed of loose sand. Old, well-tried solutions were needed, and foundations had to be built on deep-sunk piles. His design in many ways harks right back to his old favourite, the Severn crossing at Bewdley. Here in Glasgow, seven low arches crossed the water, and the details were kept simple and classical. It must have been a fine sight when it was finally completed in 1835, with its well-shaped Aberdeen granite blocks catching the sun and reflecting the moving patterns of the water. It was not, however, to enjoy a long life. Improvements of the Clyde continued, and water levels rose to a point where the old bridge had to be replaced by the present Glasgow Bridge, though some of Telford's granite facing was used again.

To set against these two triumphs there was to be a notable failure: the competition for a bridge to cross the Avon Gorge at Clifton, on the outskirts of Bristol. The story begins with a Bristol wine merchant, William Vick, who in 1753 bequeathed £1000 to be invested, with interest to accumulate until it reached £10,000, at which point he thought there should be enough in the kitty to pay for a bridge. It was never going to be anything like enough, given the size of the task and the ever-onward march of inflation, but it did focus attention on the problem. Even before the sum was reached, a splendidly fantastical design appeared from the pen of the appropriately named William Bridges. It consisted of a single high arch, flanked on either side by buildings rising four storeys high from the foot of the gorge and topped by spires and pinnacles. In the published engraving, it is almost impossible to see where the actual roadway is supposed to be, but Mr Bridges did show a three-masted ship sailing regally through his monstrous arch. Another thirty years passed after this idea was launched on an incredulous world until, in 1829, the legacy reached £8000. It was then decided that the time had come to think seriously about the project. Land was bought, and as that alone cost over £1000 it was clear that the well-meaning Mr Vick had hopelessly underesti-mated the scale of nineteenth-century building costs. But it did set the whole process in motion, and by 1830, Parliament had given official approval for funds to be raised for a toll bridge. Now all that was needed was a design, and the trustees decided to mount a competi-tion, which they specifically defined as being for a suspension bridge.

Altogether, twenty-two sets of plans were submitted, among them four from a twenty-four-year-old engineer, son of a famous father, Isambard Kingdom Brunel. The young man had gone to Menai and spent four days studying Telford's bridge. He came back and produced designs even more radical. The most ambitious was for a span of 1160 feet (354 metres), the most modest of 760 feet (232 metres). The committee now had to reach a decision, but none of them had the technical knowledge to make a rational choice. So they called in the designer of the country's biggest suspension bridge. Telford arrived, looked over the plans and rejected the lot. He was impressed by the Brunel designs, but declared that the maximum sustainable length for any suspension bridge was that which he had used at Menai, 600 feet. There has been speculation over the years as to why Telford made this declaration. Brunel's most recent biographer attributes it purely and simply to jealousy of 'a bolder engineer'.[1] L. T. C. Rolt takes the more sensible view that although that is a possibility, it could equally be down to excessive caution.[2] There is a good case to be made for the latter view, and it is not difficult to see why Telford should have been cautious. One can dismiss the nonsense of Brunel being a 'bolder' engineer: what could have been bolder than the pioneering bridge at Menai? But Menai had come worryingly close to disaster. Telford could never have forgotten the terrifying effect of strong winds on his own bridge, and that alone could have decided him in his view that the Menai span represented a limit beyond which it was not safe to go. It is also worth pointing out that boldness tends to belong with youth; caution creeps up with advancing years. Brunel was twenty-four, Telford seventy-three. We can see with hindsight that there were elements in Brunel's design that counteracted the effect of wind pressure, particularly the very short suspension rods he planned to use near the centre of the bridge. And we have the great advantage of knowing the bridge was built and still stands. Certainly Telford proved overcautious, but he had no baser motive.

The committee were now left with no acceptable plans, and there would seem to be only one way out of their dilemma. Would Mr Telford care to produce a plan of his own? He would. As the width at the top of the gorge is greater than 600 feet, his declared maximum span, he had no choice. There had to be piers rising from the river bank, 200 feet below: the logic of the situation demanded it. He proposed once again using hollow masonry to lighten the load and reduce the cost of materials. If he had left it at that, his plan might have been just about acceptable. But he was currently filled with Gothic enthusiasm, and he turned his piers into towers decorated with spires and pinnacles; looking at the design today, one cannot help thinking of it as a twin set of Albert Memorials in the Clifton Gorge. The visual effect was to make the piers, which Telford saw as structurally essential, appear to be decorative and useless. The centre span had been reduced right down to a modest 400 feet (122 metres). The committee was prepared to accept the new design: no one else was. So a second competition was held. Telford submitted his plan again; there was an entry from Samuel Brown, the other pioneer of suspension-bridge design, and others. There was also a new entry from Brunel. Against his own better judgement, he submitted a plan for a shorter, 702-foot (214-metre) span, but this involved building up a vast abutment on the Leigh Woods side of the gorge. Brunel carried the day, and not even the most partisan of Telford supporters could quarrel with the verdict.

The story of Clifton Bridge gives the impression of Telford as having reached an age where he was living on past glories and old ideas, no longer open to new influences. His vehement opposition to the steam railway never abated. As late as 1832 he was writing to the Canal Office at Birmingham.[3]

> We shall soon have a reformed parliament, where the contest respecting the mode of interior communication will no doubt be ... agitated. I am anxious to learn the sentiments of your busy & turbulent neighbour-hood, for altho' I decline taking any public share, yet my goodwill remains with Canals which from conviction I prefer for general inter-course and on this acct encourage Mr Cubitt for Canals and Mr MacNeil for Mail Roads ... something should be done to keep the canal interest alive.

Cubitt had not yet gone over to the opposition. But although Telford disliked railways, it does not mean that he was necessarily opposed to steam-powered transport. When an idea was put forward for using steam power on the ordinary roads, he became an enthusiastic sup-porter. It is easy to see why. Steam on the roads offered an improved form of passenger travel, but was no threat to the freight traffic of the canals.

As early as 1804, Richard Trevithick was demonstrating his steam carriage on the streets of London, and noticeably failing to attract any support. By the 1830s, however, there was a good deal more activity. Among the pioneers was the splendidly named Goldsworthy Gurney, whose name lives on in the monstrous Gurney stove, still occasionally found to be heating some great church or cathedral. In 1828, he produced a sixteen-seat steam coach which ran with no great success on the Bath Road. Passengers were somewhat nervous about the engine, so Gurney moved on to produce his 'steam drag', a separate power unit, the road equivalent to the railway locomotive, which could be hitched to a road carriage. This was much more successful, though it suffered from a rather poor boiler design. It was much improved by Sir Charles Dance, and this modified version went into regular service between Cheltenham and Gloucester in February 1831. There were four trips a day and the average speed was just over 10 miles per hour, and importantly, the fares were half those of the stage coach. That it was not a lasting success was as much due to the roads as the vehicle, but thousands of passengers used it.

The Dance initiative was opposed on two sides: by the new railway companies and the stage-coach owners, the latter backed by the turnpike trusts who feared extra road-maintenance costs. The matter went to a select committee, who found in favour of steam, though some of their conclusions were not quite supported by facts. They accepted Gurney's argument, for example, that there was no danger of running away downhill, as the engine could be reversed: he conveniently forgot to mention that the engine could only be reversed when stationary – not much use to a runaway. Both Telford and McAdam appeared before the committee to give evidence in favour of the steam car. Parliament, however, bowed to pressure from the turnpike trusts, and empowered them to place heavy tolls on steam vehicles.

Telford was quite prepared to pursue the matter further, and he asked John MacNeil to look into the whole matter on behalf of the Institution of Civil Engineers. Reading his reports to Telford, it is easy to see why he was considered 'a good road man', as he gleefully describes the exciting prospect of steam coaches on the road and gloats over 'the present tottering state of the railways'. He was particularly happy that the prospects for the London and Birmingham Railway were looking bleak – a touch prematurely as it turned out. The line received its Act in 1833 and was to be pushed ahead with great determination under the direction of its engineer, Robert Stephenson. In the meantime, Telford and his friends were looking with considerable approval at the alternative possibility of a steam-carriage service by road, also between London and Birmingham. It was to be put to the test in October 1833, using one of Sir Charles Dance's carriages. There were various delays, but a start was finally made on 3 November.

At first, all went well, as the carriage made its way from Maudsley's factory in Westminster on a 5-mile journey through London streets to Gray's Inn Road, covering the distance in half an hour. The next day, the real test began, with a full load of VIPs including Telford, MacNeil, Rickman and Sir Charles Dance himself. They bowled cheerfully along up the Archway Road until the boiler burst. This was said to have been a brand-new boiler, and had probably never been properly tested. By the time a replacement tube had arrived and been installed, there was only time to reach St Albans. The next day the repair was found to be ineffective, and the whole trip was abandoned.

Telford declared himself satisfied that they had shown that a steam carriage could be used on roads, and that it was a simple misfortune that the whole trip had to be called off because of one faulty part. The truth was, as Dance's private correspondence shows, such events were all too common. And while it is true that the rough road surfaces and jolting and jarring were a factor, there was a real problem with reliability. The experiment was not repeated.

It might seem that Telford and those who supported him were chasing chimeras in their attempts to find alternatives to the railways. But the steam car and steam truck could have made a real contribution to fast road travel had they not been ruled out by legislation. Because we now see the steam car as a quaint precursor of the internal-combustion-engine car, it is easy to forget that they were capable of being highly developed. The American manufacturer Doble was producing steam sports cars in the 1920s capable of a top speed of over 100 miles per hour. Telford was looking at a very viable form of transport: whether it would have stopped the spread of railways, as he clearly hoped, is a very different matter. The enthusiasm must have been strong if he was prepared to undertake this experimental journey in person at the age of seventy-seven.

Resolute Telford may have been, but there was no disguising the fact that his health was faltering. As we have seen, he had been forced to hand over much of his canal work to Cubitt, and in 1832, for the very first time, he failed to make his annual pilgrimage to Scotland to view work in progress. He did set out for a tour of the canal works in England with Rickman that year, and they called in to see one of his more curious contrivances, the Beeston Iron Lock. The original stone lock on the old Chester Canal had been collapsing due to 'quicksand', and Telford had produced this extraordinary contraption which was, in effect, a giant metal box sunk in the ground. After that, Telford became ill and was forced to abandon the tour, leaving Easton to carry on the journey with Rickman.

It was at this period that he started writing his autobiography, while trying, usually unsuccessfully, to avoid taking on extra work.[4]

Having now shared in 75 Years incessant exertions, I have for some Years past, proposed to decline the contest, but the numerous Works in which I am engaged, have hitherto prevented my succeeding. – in the meantime I occasionally amuse myself in stating in what manner a long life has been incessantly employed.

Somehow, the time was never quite available for writing, though he did find the hours to contribute civil-engineering articles to the *Edinburgh Encyclopaedia*, which he had helped to establish. He was increasingly dogged by ill health, with symptoms of internal pains that he made light of but could not ignore: 'During the last twelve months I have had severe Rubs, and at 77 they tell more seriously than formerly.'[5]

Even then, there were offers he felt unable to refuse, and when the Duke of Wellington in person asked his advice he felt bound to respond. The problem was an old one of shifting sands at the entrance to Dover Harbour, which the slow outflow of the little River Dorn was powerless to clear. The solution then in use was to impound water in the inner harbour at high tide, then release it in a great rush at the end of the ebb. This was only partially successful and Telford made the journey down to Dover at the end of January 1834. Marching around harbour walls in midwinter could scarcely be described as taking life easy. He duly completed his report, and recommended using a culvert to bring the flow nearer to the problem and to direct it more efficiently. This was destined to be his very last report, and he would not live to see it implemented. At the end of August, he began to complain of severe pains, and a week later, on 2 September 1834, Thomas Telford was dead. In spite of all his resolutions to take things easy in old age, he had carried on working to the end.

Telford had wanted to be buried in the parish church at Westminster, but the Institution of Civil Engineers had other plans for their first president: Westminster, yes, but the Abbey, not the humble church. Few British engineers of any age have more deserved the honour.

He did not leave a fortune behind when he died, partly because he waived his fee for some of his public works in Scotland, partly through his own generosity in helping out friends and colleagues – and complete strangers. In his bequests, it was old friends that he remembered, and it was clear that his love of literature had never left him. Southey was one of those who benefited – extra money is always welcome to a poet. But one bequest in particular stands out: £1000 to establish a public library in Langholm. He never forgot how much he owed to the friends who had loaned him books when he was still just a shepherd's son. As he himself had written half a century before:[6]

> Nor pass the tentie curious lad,
> Who o'er the ingle hangs his head,
> And begs of neighbours books to read;
> For hence arise

Thy country's sons, who far are spread
Baith bold and wise.

The library is still there, with a carved inscription, and nearby is the memorial of two stone seats with inscribed plaque, including a portrait roundel. Telford never forgot Eskdale: Eskdale did not forget Telford.

How can one even begin to sum up such a crowded life – how do you assess Telford's merit? Here is a man who began as a mason – one is tempted to say 'a humble mason', but that would be quite wrong. He never lost his sense of pride in a fine craft well learned, and the practical skills he learned as a boy served him all his life. His stone bridges attest to that. Yet he was not content to stay with the traditional ways; he was instrumental in moving bridge construction forward with his daring use of new materials and new methods. To move from the elegant, restrained conservatism of Bewdley to the high drama of the Menai Straits was more than a change in style, it was a huge leap of the imagination. He brought new standards to a road system that when he began was scarcely better than it had been in medieval times, and was arguably worse than it had been under the Romans. He built ports and harbours, culminating in one of the great London docks in the very heart of the city. He brought the canal age to a splendid conclusion with his ship canals and the new thrusting lines of his last waterways. Paradoxically, it was on these canals that techniques were developed and lessons learned that were to prove immensely valuable to the next generation of engineers who were to build up the railway system he had resisted for so long. And he did more than anyone to put engineering on a fully professional footing through the Institution of which he was the first president.

That would be enough to ensure any man fame and glory, but in among it all there was one element that formed his character and stayed with him all his life: his profound love of his native Scotland. Perhaps of all his achievements, the one of which he would have been most proud, and most justly proud, would be his work in reviving the devastated, depressed Highlands. He brought the people piers and jetties, roads, bridges and canals. More even than work, he brought them hope. His was a generous spirit. He was a great engineer, one of the greatest of all time. He was also a great man.

Gazetteer

———— ⋙━━━━⋘ ————

This is not a complete list of all Telford's works, nor even of all that survive. It is a selection intended to give information on all the most important structures, and a representative sample of the rest. Anyone with the enthusiasm and stamina to visit them all should certainly get a very clear idea of the full range of his work. The map references start with the number of the appropriate Ordnance Survey Landranger (1:50,000) map, followed by the standard system of referencing using six digits, the first three giving the easting, the second group the northing. Where a site covers a large area, such as a canal cutting, the third number in each group is omitted. The Gotha Canal is not included, for obvious reasons, nor are his Irish works.

Canals and Waterways

Birmingham Canal
Galton Bridge 139/015894
Engine Arm aqueduct 139/025889
Stewart aqueduct 139/003897

Birmingham & Liverpool Junction (Shropshire Union) Canal
Autherley Junction 127/902011
Stretton aqueduct over Holyhead Road 127/873107
Shelmore embankment 127/7921
Grub Street cutting 127/7824
Woodseaves cutting 127/6930
Tyrley locks and rock cutting 127/688330
Audlem locks and wharf 118/6543
Nantwich basin 118/640529
Ellesmere Port complex 117/4077

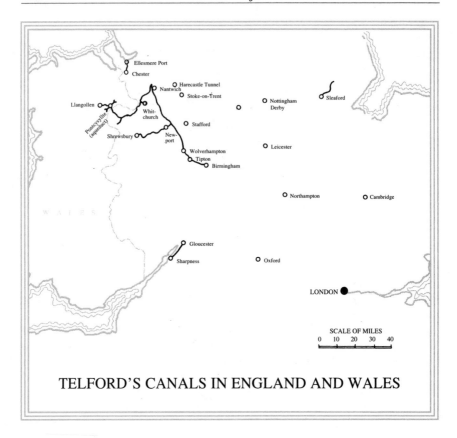

TELFORD'S CANALS IN ENGLAND AND WALES

Caledonian Canal
Neptune's Staircase 41/1176
Loy aqueduct 41/149818
Laggan locks and cutting 34/2896
Fort Augustus locks 34/3709
Clachnaharry sea lock 26/645468

Chester Canal
Beeston iron lock 117/553593

Ellesmere Canal
Grindley Brook locks and lock cottage 117/5243
Ellesmere company offices 126/401342
Chirk aqueduct 126/207372
Pontcysyllte aqueduct 117/2742
Horseshoe Falls 125/196433

Shrewsbury Canal
Longdon-on-Tern aqueduct 127/617156

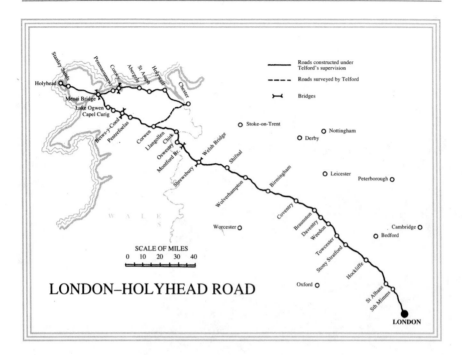

Roads constructed under Telford's supervision
Roads surveyed by Telford
Bridges

LONDON–HOLYHEAD ROAD

SCALE OF MILES
0   10   20   30   40

Trent & Mersey Canal
Harecastle tunnel 118/849518 to 837542

Fen Drainage
Nene outfall 131/4925

Roads

Roads have necessarily changed considerably over the years, though many, particularly in the Highlands, follow Telford's original alignments. The Telford road surface has, of course, long been replaced, but a section has been recreated, together with one of the original toll houses and toll gates, on the Blists Hill site at the Ironbridge Gorge Museum. Listed below are a few sites where it is still possible to see his skill in selecting a line, and often coping with difficult terrain.

Holyhead Road
The most interesting section lies between the west end of Llyn Ogwen (115/6550) and Capel Curig (115/7258).
Stanley embankment with resited toll house 114/285798

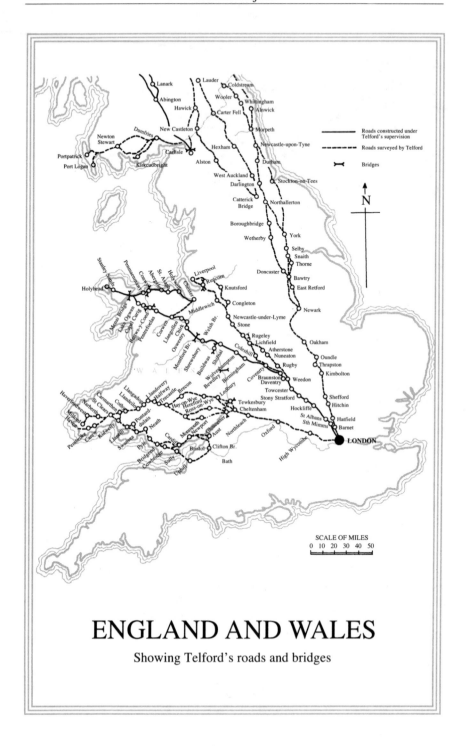

ENGLAND AND WALES

Showing Telford's roads and bridges

Highland Roads
The first was the spectacular route from Fort William (41/1074) to Arisaig (40/6586).
Sections of old Telford road can be found beside the modern replacement on the A87 past Loch Cluanie (34/1820 and 33/0811).
The Mound, Fleet and toll house 21/769978 to 774982

Bridges

The following is a selection of the most important of the many bridges he designed.

Ballater, Dee 37/3695
Bewdley, Severn 138/787754
Bonar, Dornoch Firth, bridge rebuilt but original plaque 21/610915
Cartland Crags, Mouse Water 72/868445
Conwy, bridge and toll house 115/7877
Craigellachie, Spey 35/8811
Dean, Water of Leith 66/243740
Don 34/9409
Dunkeld, Tay 52/0242
Ferness, Findhorn 27/960462
Avon, Hamilton and toll house 64/735547
Holt Fleet, Severn 138/824634
Kilgetty causeway 158/139078
Langholm 179/363848
Llandogo, Wye 162/539051
Lothian, Cranston 66/391646
Menai Straits 115/557713
Montford, Severn and toll house 126/432153
Mythe, Severn 150/889337
Over, Severn 162/817196
Shiel, Glenshiel 33/990132
Tongland, Dee 83/692533
Waterloo, Conwy 115/799557

Docks and harbours

Again, this is a selection from the numerous piers and harbours, some of which have been greatly improved over the years. Where little of the original survives, there is no entry.

Aberdeen: extension of north pier 38/9605

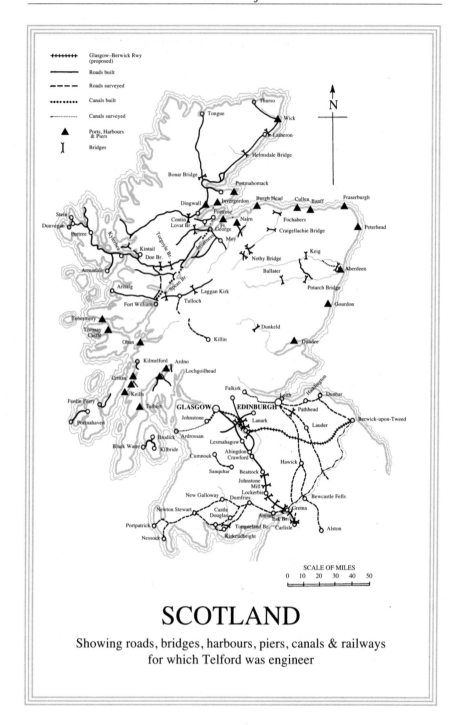

SCOTLAND

Showing roads, bridges, harbours, piers, canals & railways
for which Telford was engineer

Avoch 27/7055
Banff, outer pier and breakwater 29/6864
Cullen 29/5167
Jura, old ferry pier 61/441693 and Lagg harbour 61/598786
Inverbreakie pier 21/703672 and Invergordon pier opposite 21/703683
London, St Katharine's Dock 176/3480
Peterhead, north and south harbours 30/1346
Portmahomack 21/9184
Skye, Portree 23/4843
Mull, Tobermory 47/5055
Wick harbour and Pulteneytown 12/3650

Miscellaneous and architecture

Bridgnorth, St Mary's Church 138/717928
Madeley, St Michael's Church 127/696041
Portsmouth Dockyard, Commissioner's House 196/6501
Shrewsbury, alterations to castle 126/495128 and gaol 126/496129
Stratford-upon-Avon viaduct 151/205548
Westerkirk, John Telford gravestone 79/313903 and Thomas Telford memorial 79/297911

Notes

CHAPTER ONE: *The Shepherd's Son*
1. Letter to Andrew Little, 16 Sept. 1794.
2. Letter to Little, 12 Feb. 1782.
3. Telford, 'Eskdale', 1784.
4. Undated first draft of Telford's autobiography, published posthumously in 1838.
5. Ibid.
6. Samuel Smiles, *Lives of the Engineers, Vol II.*
7. Ibid.
8. Letter to Rev. Archibald Alison, 30 Nov. 1799.
9. Thomas Telford, *The Life of Thomas Telford.*

CHAPTER TWO: *To England*
1. Autobiography.
2. Letter to Little, July 1783.
3. Letter to Little, 3 Sept. 1788.
4. Letter to Rev. Alison, 30 Nov. 1799.
5. Letter to Little, 23 July 1784.
6. Letter to Little, 1 Feb. 1786.
7. Ibid.
8. Letter to Little, 8 Dec. 1798.

CHAPTER THREE: *The Shropshire Surveyor*
1. Katherine Plymley's diary, entry for 5 Nov. 1793.
2. Letter to Little, 21 Feb. 1788.
3. Letter to Little, 10 Oct. 1792.
4. Letter to Little, 3 Sept. 1788.
5. Letter to Little, 27 Jan. 1787.

6. Letter to Little, 28 July 1791.
7. Letter to Little, 27 Jan. 1788.
8. Letter to Little, 27 Jan. 1787.
9. Letter to Little, 21 Feb. 1788.
10. Letter to Little, 16 July 1788.
11. Letter to Little, 11 March 1792.
12. The whole journey is described in a long letter to Little, 10 March 1793.
13. Letter to Little, 8 Oct. 1789.
14. Ibid.

CHAPTER FOUR: *The First Canals*

1. Letter to Little, 29 Sept. 1793.
2. Jessop to Turner, 2 Oct. 1793.
3. Letter to Little, 3 Nov. 1793.
4. Ibid.
5. Ellesmere Canal Committee minute book, 31 Jan. 1794.
6. Article on canals (1797) in Plymley, *A General View of the Agriculture of Shropshire.*
7. Letter to Little, 18 March 1795.
8. *Shrewsbury Chronicle,* 17 April 1795.
9. Autobiography, first draft.
10. Plymley, op cit.
11. Report written at Shrewsbury, 14 July 1795.
12. Jessop to Telford, 26 July 1795.
13. Letters to Davidson, 7 and 9 Oct. 1796.
14. Letter to Davidson. Jan. 1796.
15. Letter to Little, 20 Aug. 1797.
16. Letter to Davidson, 15 Feb. 1796.
17. Letter to Davidson, 17 April 1795
18. Autobiography.
19. Ibid.
20. John Wilson to Telford, 25 July 1829.
21. The account of the opening is from the *Annual Register,* 1805.
22. Charles Hadfield, *Thomas Telford's Temptation.*

CHAPTER FIVE: *A Busy and Varied Life*

1. Sinclair to Telford, 3 May 1797.
2. Letter to Little, 26 Feb. 1799.
3. Letter to Little, 26 Feb. 1799.
4. Letter to Little, 13 July 1799.
5. Letter to Little, 9 Sept. 1800.
6. Letter to Little, 6 March 1798.
7. William Vaughan, *On Wet Docks, Quays, and Warehouses for the Port of London,* 1793.
8. Letter to Little, 13 May 1800.

9. Letter to Little, 9 Sept. 1800.
10. Reynolds to Telford, 14 Jan. 1801.
11. James Walker to parliamentary committee, 14 April 1801.
12. Letter to Davidson, 11 Jan. 1801.
13. 'An astronomer friend' quoted in a letter from Rev. Alison 6 May 1801.
14. Letter to Nevil Maskelayne of the Royal Observatory, 3 April 1801.
15. Letter to William Little, 4 Oct. 1815.
16. Letter to Rev. Alison, 7 March 1803.

CHAPTER SIX: *Back to the Highlands*
1. James Boswell, *A Journal of a Tour to the Hebrides with Samuel Johnson LLD*, 1786.
2. Henry Skrine, *Three Successive Tours in the North of England and Great Parts of Scotland*, 1795.
3. Letter to Little, 18 Feb. 1803.
4. Nicholas Vansittart to Telford, 27 July 1801.
5. Telford to Dr James Currie, 12 Oct. 1801.
6. Letter dated 17 Oct. 1801.
7. Letter dated 17 Dec. 1801.
8. Letter to Little, 14 April 1802.
9. Letter dated 1 July 1802.
10. Telford's second report, March 1803.
11. Ibid.

CHAPTER SEVEN: *The Caledonian Canal: The Beginnings*
1. *Taunton Courier*, 31 Jan. 1811.
2. Autobiography.
3. Report of the commissioners of the Caledonian Canal, 1804.
4. Telford to Rickman, 27 Sept. 1803.
5. Telford to Rickman, 18 Oct. 1803.
6. Board of Commissioners resolution, 7 Jan. 1804.

CHAPTER EIGHT: *Building the Caledonian*
1. Letter to Little, 18 Feb. 1803.
2. First report of the Caledonian Committee, 1804.
3. Ibid.
4. Sixteenth report of the Caledonian Committee, 1819.
5. Second report of the Caledonian Committee, 1805.
6. John Telford to Thomas Telford, 22 Oct. 1804.
7. Letter dated 28 Oct. 1804.
8. John Telford's report, Nov. 1804.
9. John Telford to Davidson, 5 Nov. 1804.
10. John Telford to Davidson, 3 Jan. 1806.
11. Letter dated 4 Feb. 1805.
12. Boulton and Watt, *Directions for erecting and working the newly invented steam*

engine, 1779.
13. Boulton and Watt to Telford, 4 March 1805.
14. Boulton and Watt to Telford, 2 May 1805.
15. Third report of the Caledonian Committee, 1806.
16. Quoted in A. D. Cameron, *The Caledonian Canal*.
17. Tenth report of the Caledonian Committee, 1813.
18. Robert Southey, *Journal of a Tour in Scotland in 1819*, 1929.
19. Ibid.
20. Telford to Rickman, 7 May 1808.
21. Henry Cockburn, quoted in Cameron, op cit.

CHAPTER NINE: *Highlands Roads, Bridges and Harbours*
1. Instructions for a road between South Mimms and Barnet.
2. Telford to Rickman, 20 Oct. 1809.
3. Telford to Rickman, 9 June 1810.
4. Southey, op cit.
5. Letter dated 7 May 1835.
6. Letter dated 2 Aug. 1833.
7. Letter dated 12 Feb. 1834.
8. Telford to Rickman, 30 Nov. 1808.
9. Cockburn, op cit.
10. Southey, op cit.
11. Ninth report of the Commission for Roads and Bridges in the Highlands of Scotland, 1821.
12. Mitchell to Telford, 10 March 1832.
13. Ninth report, op cit.
14. Quoted in Gibb, *The Story of Telford*.
15. Telford, *Report of Aberdeen*, 1801.
16. Telford to Gibb, 3 Feb. 1812.
17. Southey, op cit.
18. John Riddell, *The Clyde*, 1988.

CHAPTER TEN: *The Gotha Canal*
1. Dated 12 Feb. 1808.
2. Von Platen to Telford, 28 April 1808.
3. Telford to Von Platen, 2 June 1808.
4. Von Platen to Telford, 3 Oct. 1808.
5. Von Platen to Telford, 9 March 1808.
6. Von Platen to Telford, 3 Oct. 1808.
7. Von Platen to Telford, 24 Nov. 1808.
8. Bagge to Telford, 8 Jan. 1810.
9. Von Platen to Telford, Dec. 1808.
10. Bagge to Telford, 2 April 1810.
11. Telford to Bagge, 14 May 1810.
12. Von Platen to Telford, 16 Dec. 1812.

13. James Simpson to John Simpson, 1 Sept. 1813.
14. Von Platen to Telford, 14 Aug. 1814.
15. James Simpson to John Simpson, 7 Nov. 1814.
16. Telford to Von Platen, 27 Jan. 1816.
17. Thomson to Telford, 26 Sept. 1817.
18. Von Platen to Telford, 27 Aug. 1815.
19. Von Platen to Telford, 22 May 1822.
20. Von Platen to Telford, 29 Nov. 1822.

CHAPTER ELEVEN: *False Starts and Disappointments*

1. Report dated 12 March 1810.
2. Report dated April 1811.
3. Telford's report on the Glasgow to Berwick-upon-Tweed Railway, 12 March 1810.
4. Committee minutes, Glasgow to Berwick Railway, 4 April 1810.
5. Telford's report on Runcorn Bridge, 1814.
6. Telford to William Little, 24 Jan. 1815.
7. Telford to William Little, 25 Oct. 1816

CHAPTER TWELVE: *The Holyhead Road*

1. Draft report to the House of Commons, 1817.
2. Draft report to the House of Commons, 6 May 1824
3. Draft report to the House of Commons, 30 June 1819
4. Draft report to the House of Commons, 6 May 1824
5. J. L. McAdam, *Remarks on the Present System of Road Making.*
6. Quoted in Gibb, op cit.
7. W. A. Provis, *An Historical and Descriptive Account of the Suspension Bridge Constructed over the Menai Straits.*
8. Quoted in A. C. Todd, 'Davies Gilbert – Patron of Engineers', *Transactions of the Newcomen Society*, 1959–60.
9. Thomas Rhodes to Telford, 31 Jan. 1826.
10. Thomas Rhodes to Telford, 12 Dec. 1825.
11. Account by William Provis, 2 July 1826.
12. Letter dated 24 Nov. 1824.

CHAPTER THIRTEEN: *Pro Bono Publico*

1. Robert Mylne to Mr Wheeler, Gloucester & Berkeley Canal Office, 1 Feb 1802.
2. W. Holden of the London Exchequer Office to Telford, 16 March 1818.
3. Telford to the commissioners, 10 April 1818.
4. Telford's report, 15 May 1820.
5. Telford to Upton, 20 July 1819.
6. Upton to Telford, 18 July 1822.
7. Contract dated 1 April 1823.
8. Fletcher to Telford, 12 April 1826.

9. Joseph Priestley, *Navigable Rivers, Canals and Railways of Great Britain*, 1831.
10. Telford to William Little, 24 June 1818.
11. Telford to Thomas Wedge, 8 July 1826.
12. Telford's report, 27 Aug. 1825.
13. Francis Freeling to Telford, 10 June 1823.
14. Welch to Telford, Aug. 1824.
15. Autobiography.
16. Ibid.
17. Quoted in James Elmes, *A Scientific, Historical and Commercial Survey of the Harbour and Port of London*, 1838.
18. Autobiography.
19. Ibid.

CHAPTER FOURTEEN: *London Days*

1. Undated letter, George May to Rickman.
2. Telford to William Little, 24 June 1818.
3. Matthew Davidson to Thomas Davidson, 21 Sept. 1815.
4. Matthew Davidson to Thomas Davidson, 13 Feb. 1817.
5. Telford to Miss Malcolm, 7 Oct. 1830.
6. Mitchell, *Reminiscences of my Life in the Highlands*.
7. James Little to his mother, 15 Dec. 1825.
8. Telford to James Little, 28 Sept. 1829.
9. Telford to James Little, 5 Oct. 1832.
10. Mitchell, op cit.
11. Telford to Watt, April 1805.
12. Hadfield, *Thomas Telford's Temptation*.
13. 'The Members' to Telford, 3 Feb 1820.
14. Letter dated 16 March 1820.
15. Undated letter, May to Rickman.
16. John Fovey to Telford, 15 Jan 1834.

CHAPTER FIFTEEN: *Railways versus Canals*

1. Telford's report on the Moreton-in-Marsh Railway, 6 April 1822.
2. Telford's report dated 18 Jan. 1825.
3. *Tyne Mercury*, 16 Nov. 1824.
4. Telford's report dated 25 Aug. 1832.
5. Henry R. Palmer to Telford, 12 Jan. 1825.
6. James Mills' first report, 7 Dec. 1828.
7. Report dated 4 Feb. 1829.
8. Report dated 18 March 1829.
9. Telford to Thomas Grahame, 24 Jan. 1833.
10. Rennie's report dated 11 Sept. 1820.
11. Telford's report dated Nov. 1824.
12. Telford's report dated 11 Aug. 1825.
13. Telford to James Caldwell, Trent & Mersey Company, 6 Aug. 1825.

14. Samuel Potter to Telford, 11 March 1826.
15. Trent & Mersey committee report, 7 July 1828.
16. James Potter to Telford, 7 Dec. 1828.
17. Autobiography.
18. Telford to Trent & Mersey Company, 15 March 1825.
19. Birmingham & Liverpool Junction Canal committee minute books, 22 July 1826.
20. Birmingham & Liverpool Junction Canal committee minute books, 1 Oct. 1826.
21. Birmingham & Liverpool Junction Canal committee minute books, 2 Dec. 1826.
22. Birmingham & Liverpool Junction Canal committee minute books, 16 Jan. 1830.
23. Birmingham & Liverpool Junction Canal committee minute books, 18 July 1829.
24. Birmingham & Liverpool Junction Canal committee minute books, 15 Jan. 1831.
25. Cubitt's report dated 4 March 1833.
26. Telford's report, 31 March 1834.

CHAPTER SIXTEEN: *The End of the Road*
1. Adrian Vaughan, *Isambard Kingdom Brunel*, 1991.
2. L. T. C. Rolt, *Isambard Kingdom Brunel*, 1957.
3. Telford to John Smith, 30 Dec. 1832.
4. Telford to James Little, 5 Oct. 1832.
5. Telford to Mrs Little, 28 Aug. 1833.
6. Poem by Telford, *Ruddiman's Edinburgh Magazine*, 1779.

Bibliography

Beckett, Derrick, *Telford's Britain*, David & Charles, Newton Abbot, England, 1987.

Bird, Anthony, *Roads and Vehicles*, Longman, London, 1969.

Bracegirdle, Brian and Miles, Patricia, *Thomas Telford*, David & Charles, Newton Abbot, England, 1973.

Burton, Anthony, *The Canal Builders*, 3rd edn, M. & M. Baldwin, Cleobury Mortimer, England, 1993.

Cameron, A. D., *The Caledonian Canal*, Canongate Academic, Edinburgh, 1994.

De Maré, Eric, *Swedish Cross Cut: The Gotha Canal*, A.-B. Allhem, Malmo, Sweden, 1957.

Gibb, Sir Alexander, *The Story of Telford*, Alexander Maclehose, London, 1935.

Hadfield, Charles, *The Canals of the West Midlands*, David & Charles, Newton Abbot, England, 1966.

____, *Thomas Telford's Temptation*, M. & M. Baldwin, Cleobury Mortimer, England, 1993.

____ and Skempton, A. W., *William Jessop, Engineer*, David & Charles, Newton Abbot, England, 1979.

Haldane, A. R. B., *New Ways Through the Glens*, Thomas Nelson, London, 1962.

Lindsay, Jean, *The Canals of Scotland*, David & Charles, Newton Abbot, England, 1968.

Mitchell, Joseph, *Reminiscences of My Life in the Highlands*, first published 1883; reprinted in two volumes by David & Charles, Newton Abbot, England, 1971.

McAdam, John Loudon, *Remarks on the Present System of Road Making*, Longman, London, 1823.

Nurcombe, Valerie J., *Thomas Telford 1757–1834, A Select Bibliography*, Vance Bibliographies, London, 1985.

Parnell, Sir Henry, *A Treatise on Roads*, privately published, London, 1838.

Penfold, Alastair (ed.), *Thomas Telford, Engineer*, Thomas Telford, London, 1980.

Plymley, Joseph, *A General View of the Agriculture of Shropshire*, Plymley/Board of Agriculture, London, 1813 (includes article on canals by Telford).

Provis, W. A., *An Historical and Descriptive Account of the Suspension Bridge Constructed over the Menai Straits*, privately published, London, 1828.

Rickman, John (ed.), *The Atlas to the Life of Thomas Telford*, Payne & Foss, London, 1838.

Rolt, L. T. C., *Thomas Telford*, Longman, London, 1958.

Smiles, Samuel, *Lives of the Engineers, Vol II*, John Murray, London, 1862.

Southey, Robert, *Journal of a Tour in Scotland in 1819*, John Murray, London, 1929.

Telford, Thomas, *The Life of Thomas Telford*, ed. John Rickman, Hansard, London, 1838.

Williams, Orlando, *Lamb's Friend, the Census-Taker: The Life and Letters of John Rickman*, Constable, London, 1912.

Index